Contemporary Latin American Classics

Contemporary Latin American Classics

J. CARY DAVIS, *General Editor*

Abraham Valdelomar

our children of the sun
Los Hijos del Sol

A SUITE OF INCA LEGENDS FROM PERU

Authorized translation and introduction by

    MERRITT MOORE THOMPSON

Foreword by J. CARY DAVIS

Southern Illinois University Press *Carbondale and Edwardsville*
Feffer & Simons, Inc. *London and Amsterdam*

Foreword

J. CARY DAVIS

MERRITT MOORE THOMPSON, the translator of this series of Indian legends, is himself a "legendary" kind of person—the much sought-after-but-seldom-found ideal of scholar-teacher-philosopher in one.

Merritt M. Thompson was born in Hurffville, New Jersey, September 17, 1884. In his long career as teacher and missionary he has worked and traveled in many countries around the world. His numerous publications include articles dealing with the philosophy of education and practical aspects of teaching, translations of books and reviews in French, Spanish, and Italian, and general topics of all kinds. His memberships in Professional and Educational groups are varied, as are also the many honors he has received. Most significant of the latter, perhaps, is the Merritt M. Thompson Chair of History and Philosophy of Education recently established at the University of Southern California where he was Professor of Education from 1921 to 1952.

A graduate of the New Jersey State Normal School at Trenton (1905), Thompson went on to acquire his B.A. from the University of Denver in 1909, and his M.A. (1923) and Ph.D. (1930) in Education, Sociology, Psychology, and Philosophy from the University of Southern California. He also attended Columbia University and the Manila Normal School in the Philippines.

Professor Thompson began his teaching career in a rural school in New Jersey, served as supervisor of primary schools in the Philippines for two years (1906–8), taught English and Mathematics in New Jersey High Schools (1910–11), and Spanish in Youngstown, Ohio (1915–19). At two different periods he was Director of Mission Schools for the Methodist Church in Lima and El Callao, Peru (1911–14, 1919–21). Except for two summers (1939 and 1946) as Visiting Professor at the University of British Columbia, Dr. Thompson's University career has been associated with the University of Southern California, where he began teaching Spanish in 1921. Since 1952 he has been Emeritus Professor of Education from this same institution.

Courses taught and positions held are too numerous and varied to mention in their entirety. Among others, however, Professor Thompson was a member of the founding committee of the American Association of Teachers of Spanish, and his early and close association with language teaching, particularly Spanish, long ago led to an interest in the culture and literature of the Hispanic peoples. This plus his sojourn some years back in Peru induced him to try to put into English the collection of tales that appear in this volume of the Latin American Contemporary Classics series.

"Contemporary" these stories are not, in the strict meaning of the term, but still they hold an interest for the reader that is as universal and always up-to-date as our own American Indian legends, as embodied for example in *Hiawatha*. Not the first South American writer to view the Indian sympathetically as "the noble savage," Valdelomar's book continues the Romantic tradition begun with Caupolicán in Ercilla y Zúñiga's *Araucana*. It is a far cry from present day accounts of exploitation of the indigenous population as portrayed in Icaza's *Huasipungo* (published as *The Villagers,* Carbondale: Southern Illinois University Press, 1964), Lopez y Fuentes' *El indio,* and Alegría's *El mundo es ancho y ajeno.* And yet it has a charm for the modern reader that should never dim. It is a part of mankind's heritage: literary, ethnic, folkloric.

Professor Thompson's translation was initially conceived in poetic form, to be read as blank verse, but because the original Spanish version is itself in prose, it was thought best to adopt the latter style. The reader, however, will have no difficulty in feeling the rhythm inherent in each line and would do well to read aloud some of these charming tales. It is the hope of the translator, the editor, and the SIU Press that you, our public, will enjoy them as much as we have.

Southern Illinois University
September 13, 1967

Contents

Introduction

MERRITT MOORE THOMPSON

THESE STORIES are a free translation from the Spanish of Abraham Valdelomar. Several of them had been published in magazines and other periodicals in Peru at the time of the death of the author. These were collected by Manuel Beltroy and placed with others which he found among the papers of the author to form the present collection which was published in 1921 under the name of *Los Hijos del Sol* in the Series "Euforion" at Lima, Peru.

Abraham Valdelomar was born April 27, 1888, in Ica, Peru. Around 1905 or 1906 he started working as a draughtsman in Lima. He attended the School of Engineering and also the Faculty of Letters at the University of San Marcos, but withdrew from both, the latter in 1912. He collaborated as illustrator in *Monos y Monadas*, a light and humorous weekly, directed in 1907 by Leonidas Yeroví. The Peruvian artist, Málaga Grenet, also made his start in this same periodical. Valdelomar collaborated in other periodicals as well, the

Cinema in 1908, directed by Octavio Espinosa y G., being one for which he both wrote and drew. In 1910 he won a municipal prize writing the beautiful "Con la argelina al viento" in which he told his impressions of the life of a soldier, since he had enlisted in the army when war was threatening with Ecuador. In 1911 in the reviews, *Variedades* and *Ilustración Peruana* of Lima, he published two short novels, in the style of d' Annunzio: *La ciudad muerta* and *La ciudad de los tísicos*.

Under President Billinghurst in 1912, he was a political leader and was sent to Rome as secretary of the Peruvian Legation. Passing through New York on his way to Rome, he wrote and sent back to Peru several delightful articles. From Rome he sent a story for a contest being held by the newspaper *La Nación* of Lima which won the prize. The story was *El Caballero Carmelo* which is still considered his most substantial and representative work on account of its completely national character. On his return to Peru around 1914 or 1915 he published a book of history called *La Mariscala* on the life of doña Pancha Zubiaga de Gamarra. The next year or so he adopted the pseudonym "El Conde de Lemos" and started a work at the same time censorious and iconoclastic, using his review *Colonida* as a special medium of expression. In the daily *Prensa* of Lima he wrote much, calling forth passionate commentaries and more discussion than any other writer at the time. In 1918 *El Caballero Carmelo* was published, in a volume with the other most representative stories of his work. In 1919 after his death *Belmonte, el tragico,* a book of aesthetic sketches, was published, and in 1921, *Los Hijos del Sol*. There yet remained to be published *La Aldea Encantada*, stories; and *Fuegos Fatuos* and *Neuronas,* aesthetic commentaries and verses. His only collection of poetry is in *Las Voces Múltiples,* written in collaboration with seventeen other writers.

A year before his death he undertook a difficult task of nationalistic propaganda on account of which he travelled over the entire country giving lectures. He was Secretary of the Regional Congress of the Center, when, the day of the official banquet, his foot slipped in a dark passageway throwing him against a post of the stairway and injuring his spine. He died in Ayacucho November 4, 1919, greatly lamented and widely commented upon.

It is difficult to evaluate the legends of the *Children of the Sun* critically. Valdelomar was more imaginative than scholarly and in consequence cared more for the poetic effect of his work than for it as an exact reproduction of the literature of the Incas. From his intimate contact with the Indians of the highlands of Peru, he may have had access to traditions not generally known. The language of the ancient Incas had no written form, the only means of preserving history and literature being professional storytellers whose memory was aided by knotted cords called "quipus" which were, however, quite worthless in the hands of the uninitiated. The ruthlessness of the early Spanish conquerors caused most of the race to die off without having reduced to writing the traditional culture. Fortunately, there were some exceptions in the persons of sympathetic priests and others who caught a portion of the material before it passed into oblivion. At best the literary fragments are few, the drama *Ollantay* being the longest and most complete specimen. Some of the stories in the present collection belong to this class; for example, "The Brothers and Sisters Ayar or the Founding of the Empire" is well-known and belongs to the legendary history of the people. "The Outcast" and "The Soul of the Quena" may belong to the literary fragments.

It is, however, now impossible to draw the line exactly between those which have the fragmentary base and those which are entirely the invention of the author. In any case his sympathetic insight and wealth of knowledge of the Indians make his stories all very much worth while as a reconstruction of the life of that people who can be known only as writers of vision piece out the meager and fragmentary remains of their culture.

My deep appreciation is due the late Dr. Henry C. Niesse of Los Angeles who assisted and encouraged the attempt to make known the work of Valdelomar in this country, Dr.

Luis Alberto Sánchez of Lima who furnished autobiographical and critical data, and to the family of Abraham Valdelomar who have given their consent to the present use of his work.

University of Southern California
Los Angeles, California
September 25, 1967

our children of the sun

the brothers and sisters ayar,
or the founding of the empire

OF STONE was the great hall of the Incas, of stone finely cut, its gray masonry walls adorned with plates of gold and niches inset wherein glittered innumerable objects of gold, fantastic representations of living creatures; and huacos, worked in clay, bearing mythological figures, expression of the primitive soul. In some were powdered dyes, in others bezoars, stones mysteriously formed within the body of the llama, amulets against melancholy, infallible remedies against poison and disease; and in others, covered by filmy cloths, was chicha prepared by the noble maidens, the fermented juice of the Indian corn.

High on the walls, encircling the entire apartment, ran a cornice of gold whereon sculptured serpents were intertwined with pumas' heads jutting from the sombre walls beneath the heavy beams which sustained the straw-thatched roof. Before the great door, narrower above than below, and in front of which hung a curtain woven of the wool of the vicuña and adorned with colored figures, arose the throne of massive gold, exquisitely modelled and adorned with a dragon in relief, incrusted with precious stones and set upon a rectangular platform reached by several steps. Thrown carelessly on the steps of the throne, indicating that the dignitary had just arisen from his seat, lay a velvety mantle made of the skins of many bats.

In a corner of the apartment, an Indian garbed in the glittering cumbi and the iridescent plumage of the regal service, burned chips of fragrant wood and spicy herbs in a wide brazier of silver representing the monsters of the deep. The rough, square tiles of the floor were covered by a carpet of exquisite fineness, woven of the wool of the alpaca.

In the middle of the room, between the principal entrance and the throne of the Inca, on a throne of gold only less massive than that of the Master but equally adorned with reliefs and precious stones, sat the venerable Huillac-Umu, and near him Quespi-Titu, "the shining and beneficent prince." Obeying the sign from the priest, the servant put in a small gold censer fragments of burning aromatic woods from the great bluish brazier, and placed the censer in the center of the room, straightway withdrawing in silence.

Then spoke Mayta Yupanqui to his nephew. The magnificent populace which tomorrow you shall see file past his majesty, the Inca, their finely-woven garments bordered with gold and glittering with color and light were once a repulsive horde of savages like those who even today are hidden within the forest hinterland of the Andes, when the all-embracing Sun-Father had not as yet sent to the world the four couples, lesser effulgence of his Divine Radiance.

Mortal men were not worthy of the divine favor: they devoured one another; they stole; they killed one another on pretext most futile; and they drank the fiery liquid until they fell senseless to the ground. Neither on earth nor in the heavens did they recognize chief or master.

They anointed their bodies with the grease of corpses; they nourished themselves with the flesh of the conquered, and devoured even their own relatives. They drank blood and eagerly smelled the odor of human victims burned in their fires. They lost nothing of the bodies of their prisoners: they made food of their flesh, drink of their blood, and of their bones they made flutes to enliven their festivities; of their teeth they made amulets to be worn in combat, of their skulls, goblets for libations, of their hair, headpieces and slings, and of their skin, drums to terrify their enemies. They respected not the aged, their parents, their brothers and sisters, nor yet their own children.

They lacked Incas and laws, affections and virtues. They had no governors, legally chosen, and the strongest of the tribe appropriated the common property for his own uses. They perished prematurely of strange and repugnant diseases; their darkened souls descended to the most shadowy regions of Maschay. So vile were they that even their dead were forgotten. The Father-Sun himself was ashamed of his children.

Finally one day there appeared as a many-colored serpent, winding through a deep and craggy ravine, the column of a tribe on the march. The colorful garments fluttered in the cold wind of the desert canyon; the trappings, the heavy jewels, the resistant war clubs, the poisoned lances, the silver huinchas, and the waving, many-colored plumes danced in the sunlight.

Surrounded by the aged ones of the Pacarectampu, journeyed the four royal pairs, the brothers and sisters Ayar. Graceful llamas with restless but unfearing glance, moved on in rhythmic swing, bearing burdens brightly tinted. Vigorous were the men and strong, angular and grave of countenance, smooth-chinned, square and energetic. On their backs the women carried the children, while over their firm breasts hung braids, dark and long. The strongest bore the arms and implements of war: rude propellers of darts, arrows of palm wood and poisoned darts, clubs of pocha, the stone wood, hatchets of stone and copper, polished and shining, cornets, tambourines, flutes, and the sad-voiced quena. Thus they journeyed on, across the ravines and over the heights, in silence. They had come forth from Pacarectampu.

That morning, on the Mountain of Three Windows, Tamputojo had manifested his divine power. At daybreak, while the town was awakening from slumber, one of the elders of the tribe, one of its most venerated members, had seen come out from Capactojo, the window in the center, a man, shining as the sun, followed by seven brothers and sisters. The four couples betook themselves to the town and there displayed the symbol of their dominion, inviting the people to leave their tranquil fields and seek the Empire of the Sun. The four couples were named as follows: Ayar Manco and Mama Ocllo, Ayar Auca and Mama Guaco, Ayar Uchu and Mama Ipacura, and Ayar Cachi and Mama Ragua.

Ayar Manco, the eloquent one, spoke thus:

"O people of Pacarectampu, here you have your land and your families. You are meek and gentle. The Sun, my Father, loves you and sends me thus to seek you. Behold in my hand his divine symbol. See how the wild animals follow and obey us; see the condor and puma which accompany and respect us; see the indi, the sacred bird, resting on my hand of his own will. Tomorrow, the Sun, my Father, will behold us departing while you remain.

"You are tranquil and happy, but you think only of the day which is passing. Here you will die, but think not that the Father-Sun will receive you. No more shall you be what you have been. Neighboring tribes shall come one day seeking your fields, and there shall be none to defend you. For you there shall be neither hope nor ambition, desire nor struggle. You are as the waters of a stagnant pool, entirely inclosed within the granite of its unchanging shores, without the force of the tides of the great Titicaca or the proud surge of Urupampa and of Apurímac which flee, foaming and resounding, from their native haunts, and wind through the lofty and rugged Andes passing on to facundate the distant regions of the earth.

"Come, like them with us! Obey the command of the Father-Sun, and we shall go in search of the sacred hill from which shall radiate the four great regions of the earth, even to the far distant forests and the great sea, the blessings of our most sacred religion. We shall build palaces of stone and gold; we shall have laws and riches, work, order, and love. I will make you nobles and I will give you servants. But it is necessary to undertake the pilgrimage until we find the holy place."

"If you do not respond to the kind persuasion of my brother, you shall go by force, or you shall die at my hand!" said Ayar Cachi, another of the brothers.

The people recognized in the eight messengers the Children of the Sun, and gathered together in council. The youths, desirous of struggle and glory, agreed at once to follow those men whom wild beasts accompanied and condors respected. But some of the elders, attached to their false deities, resisted.

Ayar Cachi, overhearing their objections, queried thus:

"What have you decided?"

"To follow you," answered the youths.

"Who are resisting?"

"Some old men."

"On what grounds?"

"Their gods."

In a corner, three old men were anointing toads in a small vessel of stone, because it was the custom in that region to adore the toad.

Indignant, Ayar Cachi said to them:

"Behold what I shall do with your gods!"

And he approached the vessel resolutely.

"No, Ayar Cachi! No! If you but touch them, you shall surely die!"

But Ayar Cachi, alike indifferent to the shouts of his friends and the look of hatred distorting the faces of the elders, approached and seized the toads one by one, hurling them from him with such violence that they fell broken and lifeless. A cry of terror rang through the apartment, and before the elders and youths, thus spoke the messenger of the Sun:

"The same will I do with you, if you do not follow the Sun, our Father!"

Moved by the force of such manifest power, the men of Pacarectampu raised aloft their arms, and, bowing their heads in deep submission, they followed the group of eight brothers and sisters, chosen ones of the Most High. That same afternoon, Mama Guaco, she most weighted with years of wisdom, called her brothers and sisters to her and said to them:

"My Brothers and Sisters, since we are the Children of the Sun and have come into the world that we might be masters of it, let us now go forth to conquer the earth, with love, or if needs be, with blood, since it is only thus that the souls of men be moved."

Unspoken assent passed through the hearts of her hearers. Before the face of the Sun-Father had passed from sight that afternoon, they left the plaza of Pacarectampu and set out upon that journey so portentous for human weal. At the head marched Ayar Manco Cápac, carrying in his left hand the indi, the sacred bird, and in his right hand the rod of gold, symbols of his divine leadership, received on the Solitary Island set like a jewel in the mountain-girded Lake Titicaca, from the very hands of the Sun-Father, on that celestial morning when, radiant and magnificent, the Father of our Race left his mighty state and descended to earth.

Desiring only the good of his creatures, he thus spoke:

"Son, nearest my heart, go through the world and bear with you the sacred bird and the rod of gold. The rod you shall thrust into the earth as you wander to and fro, and when it sinks into the ground, there you shall found my Empire, for there shall be my chosen people. I shall guard your destiny: My rays will illuminate your footsteps; my heat shall give you life to withstand the chill of mountain wind; and when the fatigue of your wandering overtakes you, I will hide myself that you may have refreshing shade for your body and peace to your spirit.

"A people and an empire shall be founded by your wise hand. A generation of men, all-powerful and magnificent, shall be your off-spring. And down the ages, across the shadows of lifeless epochs, beyond a period which you cannot measure, shall gleam the brightness of your name. Your children and your children's children shall be dispersed after the time of your ascendancy, but your spirit shall live forever. And at the hour of sunset, when I hide myself from mortal view, they shall commune with your spirit and the spirit of their immortal race. They shall intone their hymns upon the ruins of outworn greatness when the Empire sinks into oblivion. For all must die, my son; all who live must die."

Having thus spoken, the Father-Sun gave to Ayar Manco three brothers and four sisters, seven princes and princesses of the Sun.

Ayar Manco was the eldest. Prudence was stamped on his serene forehead. In his eyes, deep and small, shone energy, while severity marked the high cheek bones and justice the thick, hard lips. The faint smile which played over his countenance as a breeze on a calm lake, suggested kindliness and love. His angular face, pale with the paleness of one who watches while others sleep, was held squarely erect on his shoulders. His was the sweeping illimitable glance of those who conquer; and his noble bearing, his simple and dignified gestures, the deep and musical timbre of his voice, all bore the stamp of his illustrious lineage.

Ayar Uchu was the contemplative and spiritual one. His humid glance lost in vague and kindly dreams of gilded twilight, fearful, taciturn, and loving. He said that the trees conversed with him and the river and the wind sang their songs to him. He talked little, but from his flute, when the moon shone, floated strange melodies, tragic and desolate.

He looked upon the stars and told his brothers and sisters that of all things which his Father, the Sun, had created the most beautiful was the firmament. When during the journey, that rude wandering, the group stopped on the summit of some hill tired with the day's march to rest beneath the declining rays of the Father-Sun, he lay beside his llamas and began to narrate to them his dreams of the evening. Imperceptibly all the brothers and sisters and all the youths and maidens grouped themselves about him. He composed hymns and invocations to the Sun. He was always forgetting weapons and trappings, which his brothers must thus furnish him anew.

Never did he wound a deserter.

Ayar Auca, the third of the divine progeny, gave to the group its reflecting and calculating element. For him was the profession of arms; he planned the combats, indicated routes of travel, directed the marches, and cared for the implements of war. In his spirit, justice held no dominating position. He knew that at times it was necessary to hold it in abeyance for greater ends. His hand of iron guided the Inca hosts over routes which it was necessary for them to follow even where their footsteps trod with withering force on planted fields. When, on crossing a valley, he encountered obstacles such as growing crops and even the rude huts of a people, simple and peaceable, he did not hesitate to open a passage for the march by destroying all in his path, thus disregarding the councils of Ayar Uchu not to kill the trees nor damage the inheritance of others. He was happy in keeping arms ever ready for the combat, as well in times of peace as when chance might bring strife. Well he knew that valor is the arm most feared in war, but he never forgot that arrows must reach their aim and darts be sharp-edged and pointed.

Ayar Cachi was the youngest; bold and unthinking was he, empassioned and violent, generous and prodigal, always ready for struggle and combat. He it was who tamed the condors and pumas. Behind him marched unreined a pair of pumas, lithe and taut of muscle. Gladly did he fight with the wild beasts and exercise over them his strength, the gift bestowed on him by the Father-Sun. With his sling he hurled rocks, shattering peaks and opening deep ravines. Riches he despised, unless it were that he might make gifts to others. He loved power over his servants, and their submission was sweet to him.

He believed himself capable of any undertaking. Singing, master of himself, confident of his strength, he passed with his lions through green and fruitful valleys. He defended the weak, punished the proud, and was first in combat. He dreamed of reaching a hill, apportioned to him by the Father-Son, whereon a home would stand, graced by the most beautiful of women, subject unto him; he dreamed of possessing unnumbered treasures, servants unmatched in skill, and gorgeous trappings. In him was the strong spirit of youth typified; in him were reflected the noblest joy of the Sun, the most powerful virility, and the purest beauty.

The women were the sum of all virtues: Mama Ocllo, laborious and discreet, Mama Guaco, bold and fearless, Mama Ypacura, self-sacrificing and kind, and Mama Ragua, passionate and sad.

The four-paired train journeyed in silence across precipices and gorges, plains, and mountain ranges. At times the rain slowed their steps; at other times the sunshine with many-colored trappings delighted them. One day, as the Sun declined in the west, they arrived at the hill of Guanacancha. The sky was aflame with exquisite coloring which deepened with each succeeding moment. Never had they seen a sky more resplendent. They ascended to the top of the eminence.

Ayar Manco, collecting his people, thus addressed them: "Let us watch our Father, the Sun, descend from his canopied throne, and chant a prayer that he may protect us."

On the plain below, the travellers encircled Manco: at the right was Ayar Cachi with the youths; at the left, Ayar Uchu with the maidens and some younger boys; in front of all Ayar Auca placed himself. All the people surrounded the chosen ones, brothers and sisters, Children of the Sun-Father. The noble and restless heads of the llamas were raised above the colorful multitude. Captive in the hands of Ayar Cachi, a condor unfolded his huge wings, and at the feet of the fearless one the two pumas, forefeet crossed in front of them, gazed with fixed glance at the fast-fading Sun which bathed the silent group in gold. The wanderers, standing, lifted their arms to the Sun-Father and chanted the sacred hymn, composed by Ayar Uchu.

That night, concealed from view of the Father-Sun, the founders of the Empire rested for the first time. In their dreams they beheld glittering lines of marching warriors, stone-paved streets between magnificent palaces, inaccessible fortresses, subject peoples, numberless herds, and festivals in which lithe bodies of maidens languorously revolved to the rhythmic swing of melancholic dances, the Sun-Father presiding over all. Others dreamed of bloody combats, with victories and dearly-bought booty. Ayar Auca dreamed that the Empire was invaded by strong enemies, and in the midst of his dream, in the peace which embraced the hill, he extended his arms, and, grasping his weapons, pressed them to his heart. Mama Ragua sighed in her slumber; some steps away, from a jutting rock, the quena of Ayar Uchu sent forth a soft and plaintive melody, while from the center of the hill, where Ayar Manco and Mama Ocllo lay, came the sound of kisses of passion.

Far above the peak of the eminence and the chosen ones wrapped in slumber, condors moved in circling flight extending over the wanderers their majestic and protecting wings. At dawn the people arose and scattered over the plain. Anew the march was undertaken and, as day followed day, the travellers moved on feverishly. From time to time they were obliged to pause for combat with tribes hostile to their approach or unwilling to recognize the sovereign power of the chosen ones. But soon the march was resumed, the dead being left behind, their places filled by newly-taken captives.

At the end of each day's journey the men of iron stopped, and before the sinking of the Sun, invoked the Father of the race. Ayar Manco advanced with the sacred indi in his hand, and with the bar of gold touched the soil again and again, seeking the chosen spot. But the bar did not sink into the earth, and it was necessary to continue until the sign should be given. Then again they sought the solace of repose in order to continue the march on the morrow with renewed strength.

Thus moving on from day to day, they arrived after great journeying at Tampuquiro. There they stayed some time, enjoying the mild and pleasant climate. Mama Ocllo was no longer the animated woman of the first days, and there were afternoons when she, reclining thoughtfully on the soft skins of alpacas, talked at length with Ayar Manco. One morning at sunrise, before the nobles there gathered, Ayar Manco opened the door of his cabin on the hill of Tampuquiro and in his arms raised aloft toward the Father-Sun a child on whom the sacred bird alighted. The child was Sinchi Rocca, heir of the divine lineage.

A few days later, Mama Ocllo could travel with the energy of the first days, and the march was again undertaken. After the rising and setting of many suns, the travellers arrived at Pallata. At that place, an immeasurably long time since the departure from Pacarectampu, so long that the children, who were then carried in the bosom of their mothers, were now able to march in front of the soldiers and play with the pumas of Ayar Cachi. At that place they met a tribe, strong and warlike, barbarous and bloodthirsty.

When the conquerors arrived, the barbarians were celebrating a festival, dancing around a fire, intoxicated with the nauseating and acrid odor of a body charred in the flames. Tied to the trunk of a tree was a maiden, at whose feet writhed the flames of a torturing fire. She, a captive, was crying out in pain.

Upon seeing the Children of the Sun, the barbarians stopped their hideous revelry, collected their weapons, and prepared to attack. Ayar Cachi wished to attack first, but Manco detained him:

"Do not kill, brother; let me first approach them."

As Ayar Manco advanced, he was met by a flight of arrows, one of them wounding him cruelly in the arm. But he continued on in spite of the wound to the place where the captive maiden shrieked amid the flames. The barbarians were awed by the boldness of Manco: who could be that man who disdained arrows and now stopped to unbind a captive maiden and assuage her wounds while blood flowed from his own strong arm? Ayar Manco tore his tunic and with the strips bound up the scorched feet of the maiden, while she asked him, brokenly:

"I am hungry and thirsty, Taita. . . . Kill me if you wish, but first quench my thirst!"

"My Father, the Sun," Manco answered her, "has commanded me to give you of my parched corn and chicha. Eat and drink!"

And he took out of his sack the parched corn, and calling a servant to bring him a vessel of chicha, he gave the captive maiden to eat and drink from his own hands. The barbarians were astounded.

Manco turned toward them and said:

"Why would you kill me? I shall do you no harm. I could slay all of you, could turn the pumas on you, could give you as prey to my condors, but you are my brothers, since I am a Child of the Sun, who is Father of all the World. Follow me, or die! I shall defend you because you are my brothers, but I shall kill you if you are my enemies!"

Far below in the valley, Ayar Cachi and his men were

engaged in combat with those who had not made ready for the coming of the strangers.

"Huayñuy! Huayñuy! Victory! Victory!" shouted a hoarse voice from afar. It was Ayar Cachi who had vanquished the chief of the tribe.

Another hoarse voice answered:

"Accursed art thou, Ayar Cachi! Accursed in the name of the puma, and of the serpent, and of the lightning, and of the river, and of the spider, and of the toad! Thou shalt be conquered!"

Then appeared Ayar Cachi carrying in his hand the head of the rebel chieftain, and behind him, bound, came the daughter, disconsolate. The conquerors were followed by the tribesmen of Pallata, whom Ayar Cachi was to pacify in spirit, enlisting their loyalty, while Ayar Auca developed among them skill in arms.

Thus they arrived one morning at Huaysquisrro, where Ayar Cachi thought of leaving the others: he wished to subdue all the tribes of the region and pass with his mighty sling over plains and mountains, transforming the configuration which he considered too irregular, hurling down the mountains and with them filling the ravines, thus making of the land one great plain, level and fertile. He thought further of joining all his conquered tribes into one united people and building a great city of stone, with a temple dedicated to the Father-Sun, with palaces and gardens. He alone must be the master; he whose spirit was created for dominion, subject to impatience to the point of violence when opposed, he thought that his brothers would never arrive at the moment of founding the Empire.

Once he had proposed to Ayar Manco that they found the Empire in any valley whatsoever without waiting to find the place where the bar of gold should sink into the earth. He became desperate at the slow pace of the conquest; he felt oppressed by the laws and methods of his brothers and chafed at his subjection to them. He desired to carry out everything at the moment of its conception. He wished not to obey laws, but to impose them, to kill the rebellious, to pardon the unhappy, to have riches and scatter them freely among serving youths and maidens, to control the world and mold it to his liking, filling it with herds and riches, women and servants.

He was the most youthful of the four brothers. But the brothers did not agree with him. They perceived that many times he ruined fertile valleys where sustenance should have been procured; at times he conquered rebellious tribes, but at many others he merely dispossessed laborers, simple-minded and peaceable, leaving behind him a clamor of hatred and sadness as well as affection and gratitude. Furthermore Ayar Cachi did not realize that one day his extraordinary power would fail him: he did not know that it was perishable, like all else in the grasp of mortal man.

One day Ayar Cachi went to his brothers and told them his thoughts. They listened attentively. Afterwards Ayar Manco and Ayar Auca counselled together, agreeing the Ayar Cachi was an obstacle to the conquest.

The following day at dawn they called him before them and Ayar Manco thus addressed him:

"Brother, in Capactojo, there in Pacarectampu, the Mount of Three Windows, whence we have come, we have left the goblets of gold. Thou knowest that we cannot continue without the sacred vessels, for soon we shall approach the place chosen for the foundation of the Empire. Furthermore we have forgotten the insignia of dominion. What shall we do if, arriving at the place which our Father-Sun has in mind for us, we are found without the sacred objects, and the white llama with red trappings, without his ear-drops and breast piece of gold?

Without the sacred objects, the conquest is doomed to failure, and the Father-Sun will refuse us his protection. Go then, Ayar Cachi, to Capactojo and for the blessing of all and the Father-Sun, bring us the objects."

Ayar Cachi, resolute, answered:

"I shall not go to Capactojo, brother. With my sling, my ax, and my pumas, I shall subdue all empires!"

"Brother!" Mama Guaco spoke angrily, "Thou shalt go! Thou shalt do as it is commanded thee. Can it be that a man as strong and valiant as thou hesitate to perform a service so indispensable? Through the mouth of Manco thou art commanded by the Father-Sun. For what does thy youth and strong arm serve if thou recognize not the law?"

Ayar Cachi acceded and they gave him Tambo Cachay, the most astute of the warriors, as a companion. But before the departure, Manco Cápac called Tambo Cachay and thus spoke to him, gravely and serenely:

"Go with him and return—alone."

In high spirits was the return to Pacarectampu undertaken. By the way Ayar Cachi conversed joyously with Tambo Cachay who listened in sadness. Finally they arrived at Tamputojo and Ayar Cachi entered the cave of three windows. Meanwhile Tambo Cachay placed a large stone in the entrance, seating himself upon it.

Shortly from the depth of the cave Ayar Cachi spoke:

"Here are the sacred objects, Tambo Cachay. Why hast thou closed the doorway?"

"I have closed it that thou mayest not come out, Ayar Cachi; there thou must remain!"

"Open the door to me, Tambo Cachay, or I shall cause the mount to fall and shall kill thee!"

"I shall not open the door to thee, Ayar Cachi."

Then the rocky ridge began to tremble before the strength of Ayar Cachi, but the door was not opened.

"Tambo Cachay, traitor, open the door for me! We shall go to found an empire and I shall give thee riches and servants and flocks. Open the door to me, Tambo Cachay."

"I shall not open the door to thee; there shalt thou perish! I am going to rejoin my people. Farewell, Ayar Cachi."

"Be accursed! Be accursed! May the Sun, my Father, turn thee to stone! May thy seed perish! Traitor! Traitor! Traitor!"

Straightway was Tambo Cachay turned to stone, and there may be seen to this very day!

The brothers and sisters Ayar continued on their way toward the north until they arrived at Quirirmata. From there they passed onward to the ridge of Guanacaure, where it was decided to declare Ayar Manco head of the family, since he alone had a descendant, and Sinchi Rocca was his heir.

That afternoon for the first time there appeared to them the rainbow, messenger of the Father-Sun, portending fateful and significant events. The chosen spot must be near! They wished to continue on, but found their path cut off by a ridge. All exclaimed instinctively:

"Remove it from our path with your sling, O Ayar Cachi!"

But no one responded: Ayar Cachi was not there. Who would set forth to combat? For on the ridge there stood a gigantic figure, barring the way. None of the warriors advanced. Then it was that they missed their brother, valiant and strong, him who would have saved them from this danger. There they remained a long time, uncertain what to do.

Finally Ayar Uchu, seeing that no one proposed a way out and that the hosts were becoming impatient for the struggle, wished to go forth to fight with the spirit of the huaca, dwelling-place of the souls of warriors, long since passed from mortal view.

"Who goes forth?"

"Who goes forth?"

"Who goes forth?"

No one responded.

Then Ayar Uchu arose to his feet and hurried forth impulsively, fought with the earth spirit and pushed the ridge from the path of his companions, but, alas, remained himself caught a prisoner between great blocks of granite. Then he cried out to his brothers:

"Brothers Ayar, do not forget me! I have been your faithful companion and have sacrificed myself that the path be opened to you! There in the valley is the chosen spot. Remember me."

Manco Cápac there established the order of Guarachico and the spot was called Ayar Uchu Guanacaure in his memory.

"Never shall we forget thee, Brother Ayar Uchu! On this mount shall be established the order of Guarachico for all of our blood and none shall be heir to the throne unless he is ordained on the ridge near to your body."

The voice of Ayar Uchu did not answer and the youth remained converted into stone.

Of the four brothers now there remained only Ayar Manco Cápac and Ayar Auca, the latter taking upon himself the responsibility of war, and the former religion. Manco Cápac, followed by his vassals, passed along the summit of Guanacaure, touching the soil with the bar of gold until he encountered a mound where the earth was soft; then he shouted

"Here! Here! Here!"

Surrounded by his brothers, his tribes and flocks, Manco Cápac entoned the sacred hymn to the Father-Sun, then raised on high the bar and let it fall on the mound. The bar of gold sank into the earth swift as a meteor lost to mortal view in the dark vault of the heavens. The people raised their arms toward the Father-Sun, shining at the zenith with unaccustomed brilliance. Ayar Auca descended to the village that afternoon, and around him the simple-minded inhabitants grouped themselves fearfully. They admired the rare beauty of his garments of spun gold and the burnished sheen of his weapons. Some, more fearful than others, remained at a distance.

Ayar Auca addressed them, telling them that he came in the name of the Father-Sun and that, if they would adore the Divine One, Father of All, he would carry back the message that He might send His son who would there found His great Empire.

"And is His son as thou art?" they asked him.

"Who can be like unto the divine Son of our Father-Sun?"

"He is shining, the Son of Light! If he wishes, the world is extinguished; if he wishes, it is resplendent with light. Tomorrow as the day dawns in the eastern sky, I shall come with the divine Son, and, if you would be convinced, come forth to meet him. There on the summit of Guanacaure he will appear and enlighten the World. You shall see him. He has brought his bar of gold; his Father gave it to him saying: 'Where sinks the bar thou shalt found my Empire!' And there in the mount Guanacaure it has sunk into the earth. Tomorrow you shall see."

Ayar Auca presented weapons and garments to the people, submissive, and ascended again the ridge of Guanacaure, followed by his twelve companions.

Very early the next morning, when all nature was beginning to awaken and the wavering shadows to outline the mountain peaks and the foliage of trees, the people gathered on the plain, skirting the foot of the mount, fathers lifted high their children, telling them of the marvellous announcement, while the children awaited, with staring eyes, the fantastic event.

That morning an unwonted joy filled the valley. Suddenly a shimmering brightness appeared above the ridge of Guanacaure, expanding slowly into a halo of opalescent light when suddenly it burst forth in dazzling brilliance. Then they beheld the promised marvel, astounded. Above the mount stood a being whose body threw out rays blinding to mortal sight. The awed and frightened people threw themselves to the ground exclaiming!

"The Child of the Father-Sun, the Son of Light! The Son of the Father-Sun has come!"

In the air resounded music, never before heard by mortal ears, and shortly on the plain, from the right bank of the stream which bathed the edge of the village, appeared the entire band of the immigrant Incas, a shining people among whom gold, rare plumes, magnificent jewels, and powerful weapons glittered as in a conflagration arising from the ruins of some age-old forest. That place where the travellers stopped was called Josco, the Center.

The founders inclined before Manco Cápac, who, for an instant placed in the hands of his son the sacred bird, symbol of his regal power. Sinchi Rocca looked into the face of the Father-Sun with unflinching eyes, and thus was founded the Empire of the Incas.

apumarcu, the potter

WIDE was his forehead, long his hair, deep his eyes, and sweet his glance. A band of silver over his temples restrained the rebellious locks of his hair. Simple was his costume, and scarcely was the whiteness of his wool scarf relieved by so much as a simple design outlining the border. No one recalled having heard from his lips a single phrase. He spoke only to the unfortunate to offer them his bag of parched corn and his leaves of coca. He lived in a cabin outside the city.

The patriarchal heads of clans had agreed to ignore him and let him go his own way, inoffensive to the peace of the Empire. From time to time they ordered from him a piece of work fashioned by his hands, or he himself generously offered something for the Inca or the holy service of the Father-Sun. The people thought him crazed. His family did not see him and he fled all human companionship. At times he worked feverishly, and then again for long hours he might be seen in rapt contemplation of the cloud-flecked sky.

Many of the workers in distant fields encountered him in the forest gathering varicolored clay or leaves for his pictures or carrying great masses of earth for his labor. But no one observed his work; no one ever entered his cabin.

Once the Governor had sent his son to learn the noble and difficult art of pottery. The youth was alert and happy in spirit. His was an avid desire to learn, and he worked hard at his first task. But one day, when the Governor was most satisfied with the progress of his son, he appeared on the threshold of his home in a state of terror. The child, all covered with mud, was trembling and, his eyes wide and staring could only exclaim fearfully:

"The Evil One! The Evil One! The Evil One!"

And he would never return to the house of the artist. For that day while the master was working outside he ordered the boy to bring out a jar still wet from the hands of the moulder. The child, hastening to obey, entered the dark interior of the cabin seeking the desired object. But when least expected he encountered an enormous shadow and wishing to escape the unknown terror, he turned to flee; but, horrible to tell, he felt his hands grasped by a huge monster who struggled with him. It was an image of Supay, the Evil One, drying within the dwelling, and the boy, in his frightened haste, had thrust his hands into the wet clay, which, as he attempted to free himself, enmeshed him the more firmly and finally fell over on him. His terrified shoutings brought the artist to his rescue, after which he fled from the place never stopping until he reached the safety of his own house.

From that time forward the potter forsook all dealings with the townspeople. He himself procured his simple sustenance. He gathered the fruits of the valley and exchanged with willing travellers jars of curious form and subtle meaning for leaves of coca. Thus he lived, free as the birds that flitted and chirped their brief day before his cabin door.

One day he sent to the Inca a serpent of clay which whistled when water was poured into it and caused such consternation that the Inca was compelled to send it to the Temple of the Sun for protective safe-keeping against possible magic, work of the Evil One, through his servant, the potter. Another day he modelled the dance of Death, and each time that he worked it was said that cries of pain came forth from his cabin, dark as an underground burrow. And passers-by avoided approaching too closely to his threshold.

One afternoon when Apumarcu had gone to the river for water to moisten his clay, he heard in the thicket the strains of a flute. Never had he heard melodies more sad and sweet. Little by little he drew near to the source of the music and saw a man seated on a rock at the edge of the river playing in solitude.

"Who are you," he asked, "and why do you play here? Where there is none to hear you?"

"And who are you who thus approach these haunts where there is only a memory and that mine?"

"I am Apumarcu, the potter."

"Ah brother, I am Llacctan-Nacc, the flute-player."

"And from what province are you, Llacctan-Nacc?"

"I have no province; and yours, which is it?"

"My clay . . ."

And from that moment they were as beloved brothers. They were never separated but for brief intervals. Together they sought the fruit hidden in the murmuring foliage. Together they passed long hours in intimate conversation. Apumarcu told Llacctan-Nacc of things which he had never before heard from mortal lips. And Llacctan related to him how one afternoon his loved one had passed from him forever. And he told him of journeys through unknown countries, and whispered his doubts of the divinity of the great Sun.

Once Apumarcu modelled a head of his friend which he carried with him because it was no larger than a fist. And so much did his friend talk to him of his loved one and so well did he describe her face that one day Apumarcu made him a head of her. One described and the other evoked reality from the words of him who carried her image ever before him. When the work was completed, Llacctan thus addressed him:

"I shall never play but for you, brother, because you alone have understood her and have returned her to me. Surely the clay in which she is here embodied will live forever. You are greater than the Father-Sun Himself, for he created her and then carried her away, while you have recreated her in hard clay so that she can never die. But I, having lost my loved one, can never again be happy. You who have not lost her because you never had her, why are you so sad? You could be the potter of the Inca. Yours could be the favor of the Inca who would bestow on you the fairest maiden of the court to be your wife. Why do you thus live, solitary and friendless, brother?"

"I feel an unutterable longing . . . I feel an inexplicable desire in the depth of my soul. I feel that I hold within myself the power to do something which would surely make me happy. I have a relentless flame burning within my spirit; I behold a series of pictures, but I cannot express them. You suffer and sing your grief on the flute making those who hear you weep in sympathy, but I feel, I see, I imagine great and beautiful things and am incapable of realizing them. Do you know? I should like to paint life, just as life is. I should like to represent in small space what my eyes see; to express nature itself; to do what the river does with the trees and sky, mirror them in its clear and cool depths.

But I cannot; I have not the colors; such as I have do not reflect the idea which I have in my soul. I have tried with all the juices of the leaves to reproduce a bit of nature, but my work is always inert and lifeless. I cannot picture the joy of the woods, nor the intense blue of the sky, nor even a smile, but in the rude clay do you not think that nature could be reproduced just as one sees her? My brothers of the Empire do not comprehend this vital truth. There is no one who understands it. The clay is crude; I can do all things possible with it, but how could I represent a man, thinking and pondering life's mysteries, how should I put into his face the pallor of sleeplessness? Ah, how hapless and insignificant are my efforts, brother!"

And he led him into his wretched cabin, where, on the wall, he showed him an attempt at a landscape, vague and splotched with rough places, but one color was lacking, the color of the sky seen at the hour when the Father-Sun, wrapped in his tinted robes of cloud, sinks from mortal sight behind the western mountain ranges leaving for a moment a suffused glow of rose-colored light. The red of the potter was too glaring; he desired a softer tint, as of the petals of some tiny wood flower or the inner lining of a smooth shell brought by some traveller from the far-off shore of the sea.

"This is not the color, this is not it, brother, this is not the glow of that holy hour."

"That color only the Father-Sun himself can produce. Do you not understand, my faithful friend? Why do you trouble yourself in attempting the impossible?"

"I wish to do what the Father-Sun himself does, what the day does that follows the night, transforming the darkness, as the rainbow which follows the blackness of storm clouds, what nature herself does with flower and tree, river and field, mountain and broad-rolling valley."

One day Llacctan had gone far in search of a rare seed yielding a rose-tinted juice to offer it to Apumarcu. And when he returned in the afternoon he found the accustomed place of the artist deserted. Entering the cabin, he could not find his friend there: doubtless he too was seeking the ever-elusive materials for his colors.

Another day Apumarcu undertook to paint upon the wall the color of the sunset hour which had for so long baffled him in his desire to express his inner vision. The sunset was like that of the day when Llacctan-Nacc had come to him bringing the sweet solace of a comprehending heart to his solitary existence. He gathered up a handful of leaves and began to rub them against the wall adding notes of color from crushed flowers gathered in many places.

"Bring me leaves and blossoms of molle," he said to his friend, who left the cabin and quickly returned with the desired plants.

"This is not the color, this is not it, brother, but perhaps I can make it do."

Then as one possessing a strange and inexplicable force, he began feverishly to rub the newly-gathered colors on the wall, while in his face was rising the flush of a passionate intensity, a hot desire to bring to pass that which he had so long desired: to paint as it really was the light and color of the landscape framed by his narrow window. Suddenly he stopped, halted by some perplexity. He lacked something, one thing only, a tone, a color which he did not have. How should he find it?

Quick as thought, he drew his knife and passionately

slipped the sharp blade across the fist of his other hand. As the blood spurted forth, warm and red, he mixed it with water from a jar and beheld the color which was lacking in his work. Overjoyed, he continued putting color where it was needed until he sank lifeless upon his bed.

When Llacctan-Nacc returned, he found Apumarcu stretched upon his bed, his blood, coagulated and purple, gathered in a pool on the dirt floor of the cabin, and the landscape picturing that last afternoon finished on the wall. Kissing the cold forehead of his friend and weeping, he played at the feet of him now dead the hymn sacred to the sunset hour.

The last rays of the Sun fell through the narrow window, gilding for a moment the clothes of the artist and then dissolving into gray below the angular face which now took on a greenish tone, and the eyes, now glazed with the tragic moisture of one whose life has flown. On the floor at his friend's feet Llacctan-Nacc found a tiny head of clay, a likeness of the potter. And he continued playing, playing until night fell as one great lifeless shadow covering a silent world.

stronger than death

THE DAY was dying. Enveloped in clouds of ashen gray, the Sun kissed the horizon. By the road to the north, which the troop, alert and joyous, had followed through the morning, they were now returning, serious and solemn, with their noble chief Maccta in command. From the jutting rock, which looked down on the river, Chasca saw them approach and stop at some little distance from him.

The chief descended from his chair, borne by attendants, and came near to the venerable warrior. Chasca asked him:

"Maccta, where is the ignoble puma which profaned the sacred flocks of the Father-Sun, and in search of which your glorious host set forth this morning?"

"We did not find him, Chasca," answered the noble

leader gravely. "As we entered the wood, a serpent crossed my path before me and slipped away and escaped into the forest. I stopped my men and ordered a fire lighted to facilitate its capture, but all was in vain. The forest fire still burns, but the serpent was not caught. Then it was that I ordered the hunt suspended. We captured a condor which I shall offer this night, in sacrifice, burned on the sacred pyre."

"To whom will you offer it?"

"To Mama Quilla; the Moon, Mother of Men, is offended. I shall offer the sacrifice in the palace of Yucay, before the priests Huillac-Umu and Huminká. It is necessary, then, General, that you lend your presence to the holy rite of sacrifice."

"When the light of the Moon kisses the walls of your castle, I shall arrive, Maccta."

The troop moved onward in silence, solemn and apprehensive. Fear was betrayed only in the expression of their countenances; their faces were pale, their eyes wide and glittering with the uncanny light of presentiment. No one, were he not the Inca himself, would have dared to break the silence of that file of warriors, which, like an army humbled by defeat, held its peace and soon lost itself in the narrow streets where the darkening shadows were already cold.

The castle of Maccta in Yucay was built on a low hill, a few paces from the river; it was defended by a wide wall of granite, encircling the base. A long approach of stone steps gave easy access to the building, at whose doors stood the soldier guards, grave of countenance, and armed with heavy warclubs strengthened by points of stone and bands of copper. In a lofty apartment, through the windows of which, narrowed toward the top, could be seen the fruitful valley, were a dozen foot soldiers, warriors without rank, whose arms consisted of arrows and poisoned darts. Beyond the walls extended the valley, green and waving, to the ascending slopes of the purple hills.

In the afternoons, when the Sun had begun to decline, long before the invocations of the people had begun to rise to the Father-Sun, Maccta liked to see the pennant-like leaves of his vast cornfields undulating in the breeze, fragile and murmuring, while the birds sang a joyous and merry song. Then he would call his favorite storyteller and have him recite legends of the early Emperors. But more than for tales of warlike achievement, he cared for romance. His imagination was exalted by those stories wherein love, blood, and supreme sacrifice mingled in one mystic and inexpressible harmony.

He always asked for that sorrowful tale of Llacctan-Nacc, the wandering musician, about whom every part of the country and even every province had its own legend. He would have liked to be that minstrel, wandering over the Empire by the grace of the beneficent Inca, crossing, with no companion other than his plaintive-voiced quena, the almost impenetrable mountains and who, rumor said, had visited unknown countries, worshiped where men had other gods, practiced other rites, followed strange customs, spoke a different language, and whose women were as white as the chachapoyas. Thus lulled into reverie, the noble chieftain listened until the hour of sunset arrived when he surrendered his soul to the praise of the all-embracing Sun, Father of his people.

That day after the ill-fated expedition, Maccta had entered the castle in silence. Chalca, his wife, awaited him surrounded by her serving-women, singing sweet and melancholy ballads of her distant people. Chalca was sad as her thoughts turned backward. She was the daughter of a forced colonist, one of the warriors of Huánuco, to whom imperial favor had commanded that all privileges be granted suitable to a high chieftain transported to Cuzco; but the proud chief could not survive his fall and in the imperial city felt himself a prisoner. The Inca, desiring to marry the daughter of the valiant chief, to one of the warriors of highest rank, selected Maccta as the husband for Chalca. One afternoon when the Sun was veiled in a gray mist, the chief died, pronouncing the name of his distant people and committing his daughter to the care of the disconsolate Maccta.

Unwonted agitation among the servants followed the entrance of Maccta into his castle. Huillac-Umu, the chief of the priests, was called and soon the condor destined for sacrifice was carried through the corridors by four pairs of attendants toward the small apartment where pungent incense and the resins of aromatic trees were burned so as to perfume the wings of the great bird. Night had now fallen. Maccta desired to display all his insignias and trophies. It was necessary to placate the Moon-Goddess, Mother of Men, for this was the epoch of droughts, when the seeding might be frozen and the crops ruined. From the gardens of the castle were brought fragrant plants to cover the steps and corridors where the priests and warriors would pass, participating in the sacred rites. All the apartments were perfumed with powders of dried duck, burned in braziers of gold.

From the granaries were brought six ears of sacred corn and from the cupboards great rounded jars of chicha, fermented juice of corn, harvested at the sacred forest of Intip-Raymi. In other large jars decorated by the artists of Nazca, there was stored chicha of common corn, peanuts, molle, and potatoes, in order that each general present might drink as was his custom in the place which he called home. Scattered about, adorning apartment and corridor, were rare flowers from faraway districts, raised in the nurseries of the palace. Floripondios, the Peruvian thorn apple, white as a long-dried bone, sent forth its fragrance from rich vessels of silver; the cantuta, flower of the Inca, presented the purple of its petals in a delicate vessel of gold incrusted with emeralds, set in the center of the great salon; and flowers of various colors and fragrance were massed around the walls. Small branches of capulies, blossoms of the chirimoya, great pomegranate flowers from the tropics grown in the palace garden, fine sprays of the ruddy molle, orchids in the form of butterflies and rare birds, white lilies, blue and crimson lilies, pinks of Huánuco scattered about in profusion, all made the air heavy with spicy perfume.

Before the doors, curtains of wool and exquisitely fine draperies of alpaca, woven by the diligent hands of the women, let fall their solemn folds, breaking at intervals the severe monotony of the granite walls. All the rooms looked out upon a courtyard, large and roofless, in the center of which rose the square stone altar of sacrifice.

Maccta wore the costume of a priest of high rank and only one article of his apparel revealed the insignia of a general of the Empire: the sleeveless shirt and girdle, the former of silky vicuña, embroidered with small disks of polished gold, and the latter adorned with birds' feathers. On his sturdy chest, hanging over the various strings of small bones and pumas' teeth and shadowing the rare beauty of that strange stone produced only within the body of the llama and serving when powdered to put to flight illness and melancholy, shone the tragic necklace of reduced heads, that all-surpassing gift made to him by his father lying on the bed of mortal agony.

This necklace was one on which were visible fifteen human heads reduced to the size of a child's fist, or a lúcuma, indigenous fruit of the Andean regions; heads of chieftains conquered by his ancestors and reduced by processes known only to the Incas. Among the heads

were those of the king Raurak Simi and his queen Raurachiska. No other necklace in all the Empire was more
admired or called forth deeper respect than that whereon
hung the heads of king and queen vanquished in conflict.
On his forehead the noble chief wore a band of silver
incrusted with precious stones, and adorned with pend-
ant disks of gold bearing the designs and insignia of his
noble position. His great ears, pierced by flat round plates
of black palm, inset with mother of pearl, fell almost to
his shoulders caressed by his hair, dry and abundant. He
wore on his feet sandals of chinchilla leather on which
were drawn two pumas' heads.

Maccta had given order that he be told when someone
was approaching the castle; meanwhile he waited in the
hall of trophies. Soon the guests began arriving even from
Cuzco, bearing the trappings and insignia of their rank.
They were received in the great apartments, where servants offered them chicha for refreshment, and in plates of
silver embossed with household deities, green leaves of
coca, parched corn, and salt; but all the courtesies were
performed in silence.

Suddenly Maccta heard the clear notes of a flute. It was
the signal agreed upon announcing the arrival at the
castle of Chasca, the general, who entered without osten-
tatious ceremony, escorted by his guard even to the
chamber of the noble. The soldiers waited somewhat
apart while the master of the house thus commanded
them:

"Remain on guard at the door." While in the language
of the nobility, he added to Chasca: "Welcome, most
worthy companion of my father. You are armed. Is it, by
chance, that you are afraid?"

The newly arrived guest answered: "Well you know that
I fear nought but the Sun, Father of all, and his divine
majesty, the Inca. But I am armed because this night I

myself do offer sacrifice to appease the wrath of our Mother-God, the Moon, offended by her unworthy children, for unknown cause."

Chasca was about to further respond, when, running his glance over the trophies of the youth, he stood as one paralyzed. A sudden paleness covered his countenance, and his voice, which before had been clear and strong, now came hoarse and choked from his throat. His glance stopped and rested, fixed at a point of the necklace of Maccta, who asked:

"What has come over you? Can it be that an aged and heroic warrior is fearful and trembles before the heads of his enemies conquered in battle?"

"Ah, Maccta! I do not fear. I remember. That is the trophy of your father and in it there is a story of love and of blood. There is the head of a woman who was a queen and who loved me. Ah, Maccta! Youth does not know . . . does not know!"

"And the aged do not forget," answered his companion. "If you are wounded by love, take some powders of huayruro, magic remedy for banishing sadness and curing ills of the heart. But recount to me that story which yet moves you in spite of your eighty winters."

"Ah, Maccta! Show me the head of the queen! Hide it not from me; let me look on it again and hold it to my heart but for an instant!"

The youth ran along the cord several heads one of which, with the hair cut to a palm's length, his fingers at last detained, separated from the others, and showed to Chasca, thus speaking to him:

"Here it is. This is undoubtedly the head of a queen; her tiny sockets are covered by closed eyelids, but how gentle the glance, and how strange is yours! Tell me Chasca, tell me the story of love."

And Chasca began:

"It was in the glorious days of Túpac Yupanqui, son of Pachucútec, and brother and successor of Túpac Amaru. Yupanqui was the very genius of war. It was he who made the great conquests which afterward his successors consolidated into one great and glorious Empire. Unequalled by the sons of men, there was, far to the southward, where the long ranges of the Andes end, near to Atacamay, a tribe barbarous and warlike, unconquerable like the Atacamas, defiant of the hosts of Yupanqui. Having received the tribute of the conquered, Yupanqui returned to Cuzco, leaving your father and me to conquer or exterminate the rebellious tribes. Valorous hosts accompanied us. Our regular army, however, did not condescend to combat with them, and with only a reserve of mountaineers, did we, after severe struggles, finally overcome them.

The principal chiefs of the tribe were slain, but not so the lesser chief, Raurak Simi, and his wife, Raurachiska. White were they, of great stature, cruel and fierce as the beasts of the forests, eating human flesh and raw fish. He was brawny and valiant, while she was beautiful and treacherous. He bore powerful weapons and she splendid necklaces of rose-tinted pearls which gleamed with opalescent sheen on her magnificent body. They were said to be the last members of a tribe of giants. Yupanqui offered me the queen as my wife and had the king thrust into the prisons of Cuzco. I was deeply enamored of the queen, and she in return felt a violent passion for me.

One day it became known in Cuzco that Raurak Simi had escaped from prison, and nothing more was known about him. Without my knowledge the ruddy queen learned of his whereabouts and communicated with him. Together they had planned his escape and were meditating revenge. One morning Raurachiska said to me:

'Chasca, my good, man, to you have I been faithful. I

love you and crave your companionship. My kingdom no longer exists. Some day I may die as my king and husband doubtless has died already. I shall never see him again. My treasures are hidden and I wish you to have them. Follow me and I will give you all my jewels.'

I followed her: day after day we journeyed southward; scarcely did we falter along the highways of the Inca. Beneath the flowering molle, within the cool shade inviting to caresses, she talked to me thus of her riches:

'What are your arms of copper and wood of the palm, itself like unto metal in hardness, your daggers and your necklaces of emeralds? I have not visited the Coricancha, sepulchre of the Incas, but I have heard it told by women, that there the walls are covered with gold and there the Sun in effigy shines as brilliantly as in the very heavens. I know that the old Emperors are there, seated in their chairs of gold and that the door is encrusted with precious stones; I know that the priests wear gorgeous robes and from the ceiling hang draperies transparent as the filmy clouds of summer, embroidered by the secluded Virgins of the Sun, and that the most skilful musicians of the Empire chant hymns of praise at the sunset hour. Ah! I possess treasures more rare; with them you shall be as rich as the richest general of the Empire. Come, follow me onward!'

Thus we journeyed twenty moons, now beyond the highways of the kingdom through regions to me unknown. And finally we arrived at a rocky ridge where, suddenly descending, a precipice dropped into a deep ravine more than the stature of a hundred men in depth, or even a thousand, perhaps; my memories of it are confused. A thicket reached almost to the summit of the ridge, toward which we climbed. Then she stopped and spoke to me:

'Do you see that round stone? Lift it up, and passing

beneath, we shall enter into glorious happiness beyond your wildest dreams.'

I stooped to move the stone, when suddenly I felt two strong arms forcing me to the ground. I raised my eyes and whom should I behold but Raurak Simi, the barbarian king! The queen hastened to aid her husband and, between them both, they bound me fast and carried me to the edge of the abyss in whose depths the river wound in and out like a silver serpent.

Then I heard shouts of war and words of Quechua followed immediately by a group of soldiers from Cuzco who rushed in and set me free. They had been sent by your father with the command to follow us, as he, accustomed to deal with barbarous tribes, mistrusted the words of the queen and determined to forestall treachery. The struggle ensued in silence and was made more difficult by the appearance of other members of the tribe of Raurak Simi who came out of the thicket. But at last all had to yield to the soldiers of our gracious Inca. The king and queen were made prisoners, while the followers were bound.

The queen stood speechless as the soldiers tied the hands of the king to his back, all the while reciting the following rhyme for his benefit:

> Perfidious deceiver,
> Perfidious deceiver,
> Though shrewd as the fox,
> You shall fall into the river.

Then my soldiers stopped, awaiting my further direction. Silently I signalled them to perform their gruesome task. Stripping him of his clothes and whetting their knives of bone, milk-white and smooth-edged, they proceeded thus: one held his head, one placed a dagger point on his throat, another at his heart, and a third on his abdomen; then gently and slowly they brought pressure upon the weapons. At first the skin did not give way, but made depressions like inverted cones in the elastic flesh. Soon, however, the sharp points pierced the surface and three streams of blood spattered the whiteness of the Quechua daggers.

The queen, pale and motionless, contemplated the sacrifice in silence. Suddenly seized by a violent impulse, she caught me about the neck, overwhelmed me with caresses, and led me into the thicket. The king, breathing yet, cast upon me a glance, frigid and inexorable. The intoxication of that embrace by arms so soon to become the prey of vultures blotted all else from my vision. When I had again returned and collected my scattered senses, the bloody head still looked at me, with eyes which, although veiled by the viscous curtain of death, still preserved that intensity of hatred which betokens the enraged puma. His body had been thrown into the abyss.

The soldiers of the Inca looked at me in silence and again were whetting their knives. Ah Maccta! You cannot imagine what I suffered in that instant! Wild plans of flight passed through my fevered imagination, to save her from the inexorable fate, chastisement for her perfidy. I thought of fleeing with my savage queen to live among inaccessible rocky cliffs, or in the thick reed grass of tranquil valleys. But the soldiers of the Inca were watching me and I seemed to read in their eyes a reproach to my inmost thoughts.

She was mute, but clung to my neck bestowing on me embraces ardent as the hot flames which encircle the huge logs of the crackling campfire beneath the cold moon of mountain fastnesses. Then I wavered. But I thought of the Inca; I realized that I should lose my rank and honors, my descendants would be accursed, my house burned, my gardens covered with salt, and my body, after its ignoble death could never enter the sacred palace of the Inti. Then it was that I gave the order in a voice strained and unnatural:

'In the name of the Inca, Son of the most high Father-Sun, do justice, soldiers, to the enemies of the Empire!'

Then the unhappy queen cried out:

'Chasca, Chasca, Chasca! Embrace me again, embrace me once more, even though afterwards you hurl my body to the river below, or leave it on a rock as prey to the condors, even though you use my hair for trophies, my skin for drums, and my teeth for amulets, embrace me, embrace me once again, once again, embrace me once more!'

And hanging upon my neck she breathed hoarse and inarticulate sounds from her firm throat, while her dry lips burned, and her eyes glittered with a strange light. I yielded. And once again we were lost in the thicket. Ah Maccta, never love was stronger than my love! No one in the Empire has loved as I loved my savage queen. I knew that when I should leave her her head would be severed from her body, and her body would be flung from the crags to the river far below, to be devoured by condors and fish. Never again would I feel her hot breath on my face. And she never loved me as during that last time, with a love of blood and death, because she was savage, because she drank warm blood and ate raw fish, because that was her last love as a queen and her last embrace as a woman.

We returned from the thicket without speaking a word and calm and speechless she advanced toward the soldiers, removed her adornments and delivered her body to the executioners, then the milk-white daggers gently, voluptuously, buried their sharp points in the flesh, tough and elastic, where a moment before had pressed my hands, tense with emotion. The three daggers again at throat, breast, and abdomen, were sinking slowly and tragically into the beloved body while she with her eyes fixed on me, thus spoke:

'Well I know, Chasca, that you will eat my body. You are fortunate! With what pleasure would I have eaten your flesh, the flesh of your body! Ah! Your vigorous flesh, savory as that of raw fish! Your blood warm and red! But remember me when you eat my flesh! Remember me Chasca! Remember me when you taste the sweet savor of my firm body, as I should like to feel myself between your teeth, flowing in your blood, and absorbed in your body, one with you forever!'

They cut the head from the body which was then cast into the river.

Night came on.

The attendants formed with their bloody trophies an escort which accompanied me, and, bearing the two royal heads, we were soon lost in the gathering shadows. Upon our return, the two heads were presented by me to your father, and today across the time and distance, beyond life and death, love and oblivion, the two heads still gaze upon me with glance inexorable!"

Chasca seized the head of the queen and lifting it toward his own exclaimed:

"Queen, queen, my savage queen, do you love me still? Do you remember still?"

Then listlessly he let it fall to the garment of Maccta where with a dull thud it slipped along the cord to join the head of the king. The Moon pursued its course through the sky, clear and blue as some mountain lake unruffled by the faintest breeze. In the apartment the torches sputtered and chattered to one another their sibilant, magic words, unintelligible to mortal ears, and emphasizing the oppressive silence of all the world. Maccta, deeply moved, drew Chasca toward him. The old Indian gazed as one transfixed at the head laden with sorrowful memories of long ago and which now looked out with imperturbable glance from the necklace of the warrior. Chasca mused in broken phrases:

" 'Though you hurl my body into the river. . . . I know that you will eat my flesh. . . . Though you take my hair for your trophies, my teeth for your amulets, and my skin for your drums and your hunters' horns. . . . Embrace me again, embrace me once more. . . . I know that you will eat my flesh and I wish to feel myself between your teeth, flowing in your blood, one with you forever. . . . Embrace me once more, embrace me once more. . . .' "

A long whistle pierced the night and wounded the silence as a dagger thrust. The guards roused themselves. In the neighboring apartment echoed the sound of footsteps, the swish of garments, and the rustling of powerful wings. The noble Chasca arose, and the guards bent low in respect before him. The priest entered with arms extended and solemnly pronounced these words:

"Noble general of the Empire, Maccta, son of Umac Umu, high priest of the Sun-Father and of the Moon-Mother, the hour of sacrifice has arrived!"

Behind him entered nobles and relatives, generals and priests, councillors, and the official historian of the family. It was a brilliant procession sparkling with colors, gems, and weapons, garments and feathers, that passed toward the great courtyard where the garland-draped pyre was erected to receive the sacrifice.

The Moon was at its zenith, commanding the scene, and in its languorous light ornaments glittered. And thus the ceremony was begun with no sound save the rustling of the enormous wings of the condor who in agitation was struggling in vain, the sputtering of the fragrant torches, and the echo of distant gentle waters, the endless weeping of the river in the depth of the valley.

the outcast

[ALONG the slope of the mountain ridge, beneath a sky of leaden gray, at the side of the abyss in whose depth the river flows on its way with noisy expostulation, stretches the curve of the royal highway of the kingdom. Below, the narrow but exuberant valley struggles to ascend the steep walls of the chasm and the bright-colored flowers garland the purple granite rocks. An ominous wind, the icy breath of the tempest, bends low the branches in the valley with force unseen and irresistible. The two ridges bordering the chasm come together at the north, their slopes joining to form a pass for the highway. Along the great road, which crosses peaks and gorges, borders mountains and encircles valleys, sometimes under a sun scorching and merciless, sometimes beneath the shade of the molle, cool and refreshing, one travels from Cuzco even to Quito where the Scyris still hold their power.

That road passes through sections of country, rich and fertile. It goes to Huánuco, the city of stone, and crosses enchanted lakes. It continues to the fruitful valley of Cajamarca, favorite of the Incas when they visit the kingdom; it descends a little and from it one sees the marvels of Chimu; then it passes on and is lost in the hot lands of the north where women are tall and beautiful and have skin white as milk. Along its course are the best inns, and the resting places of the Incas with their shrines and warm springs. There cross the paths of shepherd and fleet-footed messenger; there march from time to time, sad and sorrowful, long lines of enforced colonists, unhappy victims of the adverse fortunes of war. Over its smooth surface numerous herds of llamas pursue their way followed by the shepherd, taciturn and unsmiling, with the gloom of vast and solitary mountain spaces stamped upon his countenance. Bridges of rattan interrupt its smooth monotony from time to time, and beneath the fabric light and swaying, although tough and secure, the rivers flow with menacing roar. That highway starts at the Intipampa, innermost sanctuary of the Sacred City, and ends only in the suburbs of the far-distant Quito.

There between those two ridges which unite to form the pass to the north appears, dark against the horizon, the figure of Ñausa Soncco, the blind man. His wandering misery expresses the supreme and noble majesty of a roving and broken life, the solitary grandeur of one doomed to travel ceaselessly and without destination. His lifted right hand rests on his stick, only support and guide through his endless night, and his sightless eyes seem ever directed toward a mysterious point in Eternity beneath the dark clouds which now are rolling toward him like cattle driven in panic before an oncoming storm.

At the opposite side, in the road toward the south appear Callpa-Sapa and Saucapayac, the two shepherds. They stop on seeing the blind man, and then the awesome silence of the sunset hour is broken.]

Callpa-Sapa.
The blind man approaches, the man accursed of the Sun. Silence!

Saucapayac.
[Shouts through the palms of his hands, forming a shell]. Ñausa! On the stones is the water! On the ground is the corn!

[They place on some stones of the road a jar filled with water and near, on the ground, in some leaves, a portion of parched corn, to minister to his simple needs. Ñausa, raising his staff on high and extending toward them his arms, speaks in a hoarse voice, in whose tones is heard the infinite desolation of a soul convinced of irremediable wrong.]

Ñausa Sonnco.
Approach me not! Approach me not! I am the blasphemer, the accursed one! Draw not near unto me, whether you be simple shepherds, venerable elders of the people, or soldiers of the Inca. I have blasphemed against the Father-Sun and my very breath scorches and withers. Touch not my garments, nor tread where I have trod, nor say that you have encountered me! Obliterate my very footsteps in passing, but harken to me that the Sun punish you not in similar fashion. If you listen not to my words, the stinging blast will wither your seeding, blight will destroy your harvest in frozen fields, and the worm will fill your granaries. . . . Where are you, where stand you at this moment?

Saucapayac.
Near to the sown field, in the cornfield hard by the river.

Ñausa Soncco.
Ah! Simplehearted shepherd lads! Farther away must you betake yourselves, to the distance of the throw of a sling that the same air touch us not, that the same cloud cover us not with its shadow!

[*Then with arms extended above the valley which slopes away from the side of the road at his feet, his figure touched with gold by the last rays of the Sun, he relates in a voice deep and tragic the story of his sacrilege, while the wind flutters the locks of his long gray hair and the folds of his ragged garments.*]

karchis, he of the beautiful eyes,
and his rebellion against the sun

Every day comes the Father-Sun to the earth warming the furrow, tinting the fields with bright colors, making germinate the swollen seed, ripening the fruit of the soil, and gilding the harvest, in the due course of time. In the souls of men, at the morning hour, he places joy, in midday weariness from labor, in the evening sadness of heart, and always love and desire.
My eyes were the largest in the province, and in that province, the most beautiful of all creatures, was Munanaya, whom one day my eyes for the first time beheld. One afternoon she left her father's fields and came to kiss me while I was pasturing the sacred herds of the Sun. Between the joy of her companionship and my duties in caring for the herds, the days went gliding by and I awaited only the happy hour when the Inca should give

her to me as my bride. I brought her fine wool from the alpacas of my herd and she wove for my delight cloth for our future needs.

Ah! What endless hours we passed together at the border of the stream, shaded by the shrubbery of the thorn apple, whose blossoms like inverted chalices of snow, scattered abroad the heavy liquid of their perfume! Sometimes, to reach a furtive blossom, she would wade to the middle of the brook, with bare feet, where, her body shivering from the icy freshness of the water, she laughed and laughed, the merry ripple of her voice mingling with the perfume and falling on the fleeting waves. At other times, we walked together in the bed of the stream, and climbed upward against the force of the current, beneath the thick and darkened arch of interlaced boughs, between whose leaves occasionally filtered flecks of sunshine. Nests of birds could be seen as the patches against the sky, from which sometimes issued the faint chirp of nestlings or around which could be seen their first attempts at flight. Thus with her at my side, our arms intertwined, we walked on and on, careless of time. I picked for her the flowers which grew on the banks, and she wove them into garlands for her hair, like the sacred fringe of the Inca. Then we would sit at the edge of some tiny island in the water and there await the fall of evening to return to the city. Ah! Munanaya the incomparable maiden!

One day, when preparations were being made for the holy feast of Raymi, we were walking together through the city. As the shadows of evening were darkening, we passed before the old palaces. Passers-by were hastening to their hearthfires and a few soldiers toward the fortress of Sacsayhuamán. In the Intipampa, sacred inclosure of the Sun, some aged priests were conversing with a group of youths who were to bear the arms of noble warriors. It was now dark and gloom invaded the place. We arrived together at the door of the Coricancha and she, after we had removed our sandals to pass before the temple, thus addressed me:

"I entered one day into the Coricancha and I have never forgotten the house of the Father-Sun. In the door there is an emerald, and never have I seen another so large, and green as the depths of some hidden pool whose bottom one cannot see. I dreamed of it many nights; I dreamed that I possessed it, and that you had brought it to me. And I remember that in the temple on the cornice of gold, there is a plume of rare beauty whose like I have never beheld before or since. Then I remember that over the altar of the Coricancha there is draped a cloth, blue as the summer sky, such as could be woven only by the Virgins of the Sun. Ah! Happy the one who should possess those objects! Ah! Who could forget those three beautiful things, like to nothing else on earth!"

And she remained thinking a long, long time. Thus passed several days. My loved one was sorrowful; we did not look at each other directly. In our spirits grew an ominous thought, but our lips did not dare to express it. We no longer talked of the future. She spoke no more of our marriage, of following the long flower-bordered road to the north, toward the light and freedom of new lands. Now she did not desire to hear from the mouth of the holy Oracle in the temple the fateful words of destiny, nor did she even join in the joyous plans of the sacred feasts. An expression of mute sadness covered her face. What malevolent influence had embittered our happiness? What could I do to return to the simple and unalloyed peace of the days of our love?

One afternoon when her sadness scattered itself through the woods, and reflected back from the brook and the sky, without saying a word to her, I left her for a time.

That day was the day of the rite of receiving the sacred seed into the temple. I went to attend the ceremony, and at the end of the feast I delayed until the great hall was empty; then slipping along the walls, I despoiled the treasures of the Sun.

Yes, I robbed the Sun, the Sun!

I returned to where she had remained and delivered to her the objects wrapped in cloth.

"What is it, Karchis?" she said to me, speaking listlessly, dreaming of the things she believed unobtainable.

"The emerald, the cloth, and the plume from the Temple of the Sun."

She looked at me terrified, as if awakening from a dream, as if realizing the impossible; then fled as one crazed into the wood, exclaiming as she ran:

"Touch me not! Touch me not, Karchis! Look not upon me! Speak not to me! And approach not near unto me! You have stolen from the Sun!"

Then occurred I know not what. I lost my sense of things about me; I ran after her, but I did not feel the earth beneath my feet. I followed her, I know not why, for now that I was lost, she abandoned me. A desire for vengeance took possession of me. I could not lose her; she was so beautiful! Her complexion was faintly tinted with rose, as the color of clay baked in the huacos, sacred vessels of the Inca; her body gently rounded as that of a child. Night itself had given the color to her hair and had lighted in her cheeks the glow of a distant hearthfire, and the band of silver which girded her forehead with the cords falling over her temples. . . .

But she fled as one possessed by Supay, the Evil One, and was soon lost among the crags and thickets, leaving me alone with the Sun. When I again sought to catch her, she hid herself anew, finally appearing on a sharp, stony ledge which dropped abruptly to the river. I wanted to seize her and did not know whether to slay her or enfold her with the embraces of love even though I die thereupon. She fled, jumping feverishly from rock to rock, leaving tattered shreds of her garments on the brambles and uttering fearful cries which rent my very soul. Her hands and her sides, spattered with blood, still exhaled the perfume of love to my half-crazed senses. Out of breath I followed her and saw finally that she was faint. Soon she fell inert upon a large rock near the river. Then with fury I shouted to her:

"Do not flee! Now you cannot flee! You are going to be mine! And when I have placed my hands on your flesh, and when you have received my breath, lost will you be forever, even as I, accomplice of mine, who drove me to the horrible crime! Await me!"

I went toward her and was about to take her in my arms when, moved by a sudden impulse, she gave a start, and slipping on the stone, fell into the river. Her body in its fall struck a projecting crag, spattering it with blood. The water formed a wide circle upon receiving her as she disappeared from sight forever. A great stain, rose-tinted foamy, appeared in the waters and spread toward the other shore, becoming fainter and fainter.

Then violent wrath pervaded my whole being and I felt myself possessed by Supay, the Evil One. I wished to struggle with something, with someone. My loved one I had lost. I wished to break in pieces with my hands the unyielding rock and my nails scratched in vain its cold surface. I sank my teeth into the bark of trees, for no one remained on earth but the Sun and me. The Sun, voiceless, was avenging himself inexorable and merciless, but I cried to him aloud:

"Cruel! Cruel! I loved her as no one has ever loved before. Before the joy of possessing her, your treasures are worthless. Your emeralds and plumes are pale and color-

less beside her beauty. She was the most beautiful creature on which fell your light as it was shed abroad over
the world. My eyes were more beautiful even than your
light, and because of them you were envious of me. You
have stolen her from me, but I shall be avenged. I will
desecrate the snow of your mountain peaks; I will sacrifice your llamas and, with their blood, I will pollute the
purity of the sacred snow. I shall be avenged!"

Then, with my soul filled with hatred and my senses
blinded by my desire for vengeance, I went in search of
the herd of the Sun. I myself led them out of the royal
fields and onward and upward to the lofty heights, pasturing them by the way. I journeyed a long, long time
until I reached the very crest where the snow is the
whitest and purest of all earthly things. From that point
of eminence one could look down on the sacred city seen
in the distance, and on towns, valleys, dwellings, and
flocks. The wretched Children of the Sun inspired me
with pity as I looked down on their humble possessions.
They, unhappy ones, as yet were ignorant of my misfortune. They would never contend with the Sun, but in
peace and submission descend to a gentle old age. I had
cared well for the herd hitherto and had selected six of
the finest animals to be a votive offering at the feast of
Cápac Raymi, but the Sun, unmindful of the sacrifice,
was about to defend himself and chastise my effrontery.
When I found myself at the highest point of that bleak
region, surrounded by the herd, white and trembling
with fear, I took out my hunting knife. But, behold, at
the moment when my unhallowed feet came to the point
of treading the sacred snow, the Sun darkened the sky;
great heavy clouds descended even to my very head and
enwrapped the herd and me in a dense mist, out of which
appeared a flock of condors, sent by Him, as if the very
blackness of the clouds themselves was condensing into

life. Swinging in enormous circles about my head, they terrified the llamas, who fled in all directions and scattered as a flock of wood doves before the great and menacing wings. I tried to restrain them, but they stopped only when they reached the calm pastures of the valley below.

Then I was alone with the cloud of vengeance-bearing condors, divinely appointed, who bore me to the ground by the strength of their powerful wings, enveloping me in darkness and confusion. Their beaks and claws, sharper than the keenest weapon, began to sink into my flesh and to rend my body. Then only was it that I began to feel fear of the Sun, and, convinced of his punishment inexorable, I cried out to him:

"My Father! I will not defend myself. I will permit them to destroy me and prey upon the flesh of my body, but let me once again upon earth behold the face of my beloved! Return her to me!"

I could speak no more. The cloud of condors left me for an instant, rising toward the sky, now of deepest azure. The Sun glared with a strange light, and one of the condors flew down and picked out one of my eyes, and another following, robbed me of the other, bearing off the light of my day. Thus the last ray of the Sun was extinguished for me, leaving me in darkness forever. I knew by the rustle of wings that the condors were departing, they who were carrying with them my orbs of vision. The roaring of their wings grew fainter and fainter, and at last a hopeless silence reigned.

Only upon earth now remained the outraged Sun, whom I could not see, and I, whom his rays no longer warmed, seek my eyes, shepherds, in the highway of the Inti! There they appear when the Moon sheds her pale light over the world, for they cannot bear the stronger effulgence of the Sun. They are near to the warrior Chasca.

. . . But I do not know, how should I know? Whether my eyes from their starry heights look upon the Moon, whether they look down into the river, or whether they see pass my miserable body, accursed and blasphemous, in the midst of an eternal night. . . . Tell me shepherds, do you see my eyes in the blue vault of the heavens?

Callpa-Sapa.
They are very beautiful and are near to the moon!

Ñausa Soncco.
At what are they looking? Observe closely, shepherds, the direction of their gaze!

Saucapayoc.
Their gaze falls on the river!

Ñausa Soncco.
Still they pursue her. Pass on, pass on without touching me. Pass afar. Afterward you will efface my footsteps and say not that you have beheld me. . . . Pass on not nearer than the throw of a sling. . . . Pass on!

Callpa-Sapa.
Ñausa! On the stones is the water! And on the ground is the corn!

Ñausa Soncco.
Where are you now?

Saucapayoc.
Near to the sown field. In the cornfield which slopes to the river.

Callpa-Sapa.
Whither do you journey?

Ñausa Soncco.
Toward the night! Toward the night! Never-ending and all-pervading.

The Echo.
Toward the night! Never-ending and all-pervading.

[*And they go their way in opposite directions along the royal high road of the kingdom.*]

the snow shepherd and his flock

IN THE reign of Túpac Inca Yupanqui, Ritti-Kimi, brother of the Inca, was one of his favorites. He used arrows and weapons equal to those of his royal brother and in the afternoons spent long hours in conversation with him. All were happy in the kingdom. Pácaric had made conquests for his Inca, had collected animals of great rarity for his apartments, and precious stones for his headband, symbol of his royal authority.

One afternoon, from the terrace of the royal palace, the two noble brothers watched together the Sun descending over the distant sea, covering the sky with a ruddy glow as of a flame from the fires of the sacred altar. They watched attentively as the Sun slowly dropped behind the horizon without enwrapping himself in clouds, a happy omen for the Inca. The orb of day was just about to disappear when a tiny gilded cloud approached the sacred disk and almost touched its rim. The Inca grew pale. Now the cloud wisp changed its direction and touched not the holy face, while the two nobles absorbed with a feverish interest scarcely breathed. Now were left but a few moments . . . now . . .

"At last!"

"A blessed fortune awaits you!"

"I am satisfied, even joyful at the outcome. Ask of me what you will and today I shall grant it to you."

"You will grant to me, sir and brother, what I ask of you today?"

"I shall grant it to you! Speak!"

"I desire to behold the sacred Virgins of the Sun!"

The Inca again grew pale. The request was bold beyond his wildest imagination; there was not precedent for such a request and him who dared to voice it in words would they have hanged in the public plaza.

"You have not sought riches, not castles, nor estates; nor fortune, nor honors. You have not stopped at gold unmeasured, a woman of my concubines, or one of my slaves. Why do you ask what never before has been sought? Why do you desire that your eyes behold what never before human eyes have beheld? Seek of me what you will: my treasures are yours, my slaves and my concubines, my weapons and my garments, my sheep and my llamas. But ask me not for that which is not mine to grant!"

"Son of the most high Sun-Father, you have promised it to me. You will not deny that you promised what I should desire. You can refuse to fulfill your promise and command that in your presence I be hanged; but, if it be that men deceive, remember that the gods are not deceived by the wiles of men. You will not wish to try to deceive them! You will keep your august word! You have

promised, noble Child of the Sun."
The Inca felt himself lost before the words of his brother.
His face clouded and with gaze downcast he answered:
"Be it so!"

.   .   .   .

It was late in the afternoon when the noble entered the
sacred place. He was not to talk to the chosen ones, but
he might visit all parts of the abode and look upon all the
Virgins. His eyes were enchanted. Then as a flash of
summer lightning passing between the clouds of a trou-
bled sky, from the dark depths of the eyes of her whom
they called Yipay came an answering and passionate
glance which changed for him the world forever. But no
word was spoken.

.   .   .   .

The Inca made his brother shepherd of the sacred flocks
of the Sun and chose for himself from among the Virgins
of the Sun (privilege of his divine and royal might) one
who should enter the royal household, most recent and
beautiful of maidens to become betrothed to his Majesty,
and share the honors of his lofty position.

.   .   .   .

"Whence come you, traveller?"
"From the Sacred City."
"Know you the noble Ritti-Kimi, brother of the Inca?"
"Yes, for many moons he has been shepherd of the flocks
of the Sun, far from the Sacred City."
"What is the news of the Kingdom?"
"A great feast is taking place. The nuptials of the Inca
and Yipay, Virgin of the Sun."
The questioner continued his way toward the City and
met a messenger, fleet of foot, bearing dispatches be-
tween cities of the Empire.
"Whence come you?"

"From the City of Gold."

"What news from the City?"

"A great feast. Today the Inca takes a new wife."

The questioner hastened on, almost treading upon an aged man bowed low in the dust of the royal highway.

"Whence come you?"

"From the City of the Inca."

"What news bring you from the City?"

"The marriage of a Virgin of the Sun."

Then, his soul torn asunder, grief in his eyes, his hands trembling as of one palsied by sudden shock, he turned and strode toward the hill at the foot of the sierras, abandoning his journey to the Sacred City. As he turned he saw a group of travellers.

"Whither go you?"

"We travel to Cuzco for the nuptials of the Virgin of the Sun. These are gifts from the Province."

Then he fled to the mountains, as gloom, like the shadow of night, enveloped his spirit. Arriving at the familiar pasture, he drove the flock toward the snowline of distant peaks, upward and upward. The sheep, huddled together meek and white, ascended slowly, peaceable, silently, upward toward the high mountains. One day passed, two days, and then at last they arrived at a virgin snowfield. Already his hands were frozen and his tongue swollen; the cold entered into his very bones, for the Sun glittering on the snow lent him no warmth; and there was a roaring sound in his ears because he had eaten nothing during the long climb.

Then he caught a sheep and prepared to commit the horrible crime of butchery and avenge himself on the Inca, his brother and rival. He wished to pollute with blood the perpetual snows. The Sun, perceiving the shepherd in the midst of the sacred flock preparing the bloody sacrifice, hid his dazzling face in an instant and let loose a raging tempest, hurling over the mountains in fury, snow, snow, spotless snow. When the Sun again unveiled his face, the shepherd and his flock had become snow.

He had loved the Virgin with so strong and pure a love that the Sun-Father himself could not overcome that passion and grief, and when he shows his face over the mountain, against his will his rays always melt a little of the icy statue and water runs down from the head of the lover, seeking first a narrow channel, then a brook, a stream, afterward a river, and at last the sea on whose bosom those tears are scattered over all the world, tears of the lover's weeping. And always he weeps when the sun shines.

When you ascend the mountain and see the snow on the peak, you will find the white snowflock, and in their midst the poor shepherd. The lover has never returned to the world, and he will weep eternally, while there is snow, while there are mountains, and when the Sun appears and makes his tears to flow.

the soul of the quena

FROM the small terrace by the palace the Inca saw the Moon rise in the splendor and peace of the night and heard the same rare melody that he had heard by the royal highway during the late afternoon. He had commanded his escort to halt and, while his professional storytellers blew the note of inquiry on their flutes, certain of his attendants scattered into the valley, but the Inca did not learn whether that strange and doleful music proceeded from man or from bird. Now he heard it more clearly, though still imperfectly, and he listened intently to catch it even more distinctly.

It was a strain where joy and sorrow mingled, as a sweet reproach, as a complaint murmured in a low voice, notes which enwrapped the spirit, and penetrated into the nerve cords as a dagger thrust, which awakened unburied

memories and griefs not yet covered by the hallowing
and merciful hand of time, at whose sound words died on
one's lips, and tears came to the eyes, and in the profound depths of the soul welled up something akin to
desire, a yearning toward that all-pervasive world soul,
which in its depths is always tragic, even in its joys. Was
it a bird from some remote and unknown place? Was it a
man pouring out his very soul? To his guards Sinchi
Rocca gave order to quench the burning resins and retire.
"How the melody floats, how it vibrates, and what a
world of sadness it bears." Thus he spoke to his wife,
Coya Chimpo, seated at his side, who answered:
"So divine is that music, my lord and husband, that it
seems not the song of man nor the sound of a quena.
One would say that it is a bird come to weep out its soul
beneath the Moon. During these nights, from far-off
mountains and valleys come rare birds to sing in the
gardens of the palace. Yesterday I saw a tiny bird, red as a
wound, that rested in the sacred cornfields."
The noble monarch arose. Deliberately and calmly he
surveyed from the terrace the Imperial City. It spread
below with its temples and palaces. Ruddy lights marked
the location of the four plazas and the four great highways. In front stood the Coricancha, guarded by Villac
Umus and his noble warriors, and within it rested the
divine treasure, the image of the Sun, flanked by the
double row of mummies of the Emperors. Before the
massive temple extended the Intipampa, great and sacred
plaza, center of the Empire, around which stood the
palaces of the nobles.
Nearby, facing the Amarucancha, place of serpents, rose
the temple of the Chosen Ones, Virgins of the Sun,
within the unbroken walls of heavy stone. Some distance
to the right, surrounding the plaza of Cuntisuyu, could
be seen the prisons on the far side of the river; and on the

near side the royal fields. On the opposite side of the city were barracks, dwellings for the unfortunate, corrals for beasts as yet unbroken to cargo, and some palaces of nobles. Farther away beyond the walls the fresh valley slept beneath the sapphire sky of the tranquil night, while the moon let fall her mystic rays, and a perfumed breeze ascended like incense to her from a silent World. Quietly the Inca seated himself in his chair of black palm incrusted with gold.

"If he who draws forth that melody be a man, I should like to have him in the palace, if a bird, in my gardens."

"Command it so, my lord."

"If he were a man it would be easy to take him into my service; but if he be a bird, my will avails nothing, since his kind are bearers of the pomp of the Sun, my Father, chosen by him and sacred to his honor."

Suddenly the Coya, making a gesture of supplication, exclaimed:

"Listen, Son of the Most High!"

The Inca concentrated his attention; his face showed curiosity, then admiration, mingled at first with a shadow of doubt, but clearing suddenly, he spoke and rubbed his hands with the joy of a child:

"I have it! I have it! It is a quena! Seek out and bring to me the man who plays!"

Groups of serving-men were burning aromatic essences in the half-light of the Moon. At a sign from the Inca, they went out quickly to obey his command, while others took their places and continued burning the resins. All were silent for a time. Then the quena sounded, nearer and nearer. The calls of the guards rang out from post to post. Meanwhile the Coya thus spoke:

"If he is a man, it must be Llacctan-Nacc; but he has not been seen. Kuychy, my maid, has told me that Llacctan is not in the kingdom. The shepherds say that the Father-Sun took him from the Empire to sing in his mansions beyond the great sea. The white women of the North say that Mama Quilla has banished him that he no longer make men to die with his songs of infinite sorrow. The fishermen of the Sacred Lake say that he wanders at night on the Solitary Isle; the laborers say that the birds, envious of his music, pierced his eyes, and he, blinded, fell into the river; the guardians of the Amarucancha relate that, at the sound of his flute, the serpents followed and devoured him; and the messengers of the Empire declare that they hear his melodies at night in the depths of the forests."

The voices of the guards were heard and shortly there appeared a group of noble retainers leading an Indian. In the royal presence all bent low, a tiny burden upon each back, symbol of humble submission, while the Indian, trembling, stammered:

"The humblest of your servants, Viracocha!"

"Lift him up, let him, approach, and you may retire," the Inca commanded, and remained unattended with the Coya and the musician, who was poorly covered by a ragged tunic. The remainder of his costume betokened his rude and wandering life: torn sandals, a rough staff of heavy wood, his hair thick and tangled, held at the forehead by a band in the manner of a crown and from the neck hung, on a long cord, the flute of five notes.

"Who are you?" asked the Inca.

"I am, Viracocha, from the district next to that of the Imperial City."

"Who has taught you to play the flute? Why is your song so mournful?"

"No one has taught me, Most Powerful One! It was grief! I weep for the loss of my beloved."

"The Inca, your father, wishes to be friendly to you; the Son of the Father-Sun will give you what you desire. Ask.

From today you shall live in my palace and in my garden, where your soul will forget its pain and your quena will give joy to the castle. You shall play on the quena without hindrance. Hear you my words? I am going to make you happy!"

"That I can never be, Son of the most High. Even you cannot bring her back from the palace of the Sun . . . but you can lessen my misfortune . . . I ask of you one thing . . ."

"Speak."

"Grant me ever the freedom of the Empire, to pass the frontiers, to journey to remote places, to wander over all roads. Command that no one close to me the highway, and that no one in your kingdom prevent my playing the quena. Make me believe that all the world is mine, and, knowing that my life belongs to you, let me believe, O Son of the Most High, that I may devote it to my grief."

"I will give you servants, I will make you a noble; you shall draw near to my throne and march in my retinue. You shall have soft garments woven from the fine wool of young alpacas, and servants to fulfill your least desire. But you shall continue to play the quena."

"My Father! My Father! Let me wander through the world! I will sing songs to Inti in your name. On the largest trees I will carve your symbols, and on the highest rocks I will place your colors. I will hunt bats for your imperial robe; I will teach the heads of families in distant provinces to pronounce your name and respect your deeds; and farther yet in the depths of the forests, where the voice of your storytellers is not heard, I will scatter the fame of your exploits, at the dawn of each day when the Sun, your Father, begins to appear. But let me depart!

If I remain in your castle, my songs will not please you nor my sorrow touch your heart. Do you desire that I be happy and my quena weep? Give me not feasts nor riches, servants nor palaces. Grief is not made. Grief is. One does not weep to divert others. Sorrow is in the light of the Moon, in the shadow of branches, in the silence of nature; in the gray of clouds which gather into opaque masses at the summits of mountains when it rains: there is grief. In the cold wind, the cutting blast of the tempest, in the rumbling of thunder, in the rain falling in torrents incessant, in the sacred snow, in the river that tears its bed and reddens its water with clay, in the vivid flash of the lightning: there abides sorrow.

But in your gardens, Son of the Most High, it abides not. Grief is immense as the sea, proud as the condor, many-colored as the wood. You know not the pangs of sorrow . . . Let me go, Child of the Sun, Powerful One, Kin to the Creator of all things; take not from me the only thing which remains to me in life, my affliction. Break not the spell of my quena, destroy me not!"

"You are, and you are not, of my kingdom. Go through the world, Divine Wanderer, wear this sign of the Inca that no one oppose you in your course. It is a plume from my diadem. Farewell! Go in peace!"

"Farewell! Farewell!"

And speaking thus the musician bowed low and kissed the floor at the feet of the monarch. The soldiers turned toward him, and, escorted by them, he descended the steps of the palace. The guards returned to their post. The resins in the brasiers were renewed and soon beneath the serene and silent Moon once again from the distant canebrake came the mournful and desolate echo of the quena.

"Such sweet sadness! Such sweet sadness!" Murmured the Inca, turning to his Queen.

"Farewell!" sounded from afar the voice of the artist. The Moon passed beneath a cloud.

the wandering minstrel

ALONG the edge of the sown fields Chasca advanced silently. The day had begun to darken; the Sun already slept beyond the distant sea, and he must hasten to reach the castle before the light was gone. He decided to leave the fields and follow a road now deserted except by laborers, somewhat delayed, who were hurrying toward the town desirous of arriving at their hearthfires before complete darkness should overtake them. Soon he found it necessary to hide himself in order to avoid a large group who, as they hurried along, were talking of the hunting party of Maccta. With loud words and heated tones, they talked and argued about the fates and oracles, and their relations to the world of men. As the last one passed, Chasca again set forth.

It was nearly night, and the old warrior hurried on in

silence. He must reach the end of the road by the river's
edge, and follow the path along the bank until he came
to the bridge, cross it and at last enter the tiny valley in
whose depths stood the castle of the noble youth. Near-
ing the river, he began to hear the roar of the water
flowing over rounded pebbles and against rocky points
jutting into the stream; and, winding itself into the roar
of the water, an echo, barely perceptible, and gentle as a
sigh of distant music. At first, Chasca did not notice it,
but, as he approached nearer to the edge of the river, the
notes, above the gentle contention of rocks and water,
gradually became clearer: a sound as of a complaint without reproach, a soft lament, a sorrow supreme and incon-
solable, which struck to the depths of the listener's soul
and renewed the pain of long-forgotten wounds, healed
by the soothing hand of time.

As Chasca advanced he became fascinated without desiring it, in that music awakening memories buried deep in
his heart. It recalled to the Indian warrior his long-dead
sorrows, his distant pleasures now veiled by the years
with a melancholy haze. He saw pass by as in a procession
his parents and the friends of his childhood; his entrance
into the Military School, and his part in the military
expeditions of Cuntisuyu under the great and noble
Huaina Cápac; his exploits, his title, bestowed by the
Inca, of General of the Empire; his loves, whose fires
were long since burned to ashes, cold and gray, the
women dear or forgotten; his riches in heaped futility, to
bring happiness; and his seventy winters nobly borne and
respected throughout the Empire.

Never before had he recalled his past, nor had the future
brought him misgiving, but now the sound of a distant
flute on a night set apart for a sacrifice to the Moon,
Mother of Men, in the midst of fields and woods, far-
extended and silent, took possession of him and com-

pelled him to reflection. Was it his soul, sensitive to pain, which was affected by a song of war? Was it some great musician capable of making him feel and of arousing these sensations by the power of a great and divinely bestowed gift?

If it were a musician, then only could it be Llacctan-Nacc, the flute player whose notes brought sadness to the very soul. But he was not in the Empire and perhaps no longer even in this world; and yet, who but he could bring forth the melody which now flowed from the flute? The voice of the quena became silenced and the Moon was enwrapped in great clouds, dark and ominous. Chasca sensed the way among the rocks and passed onward without mishap.

On reaching the river, he saw on a point of jutting rock far above him a human figure. He approached to within some twenty paces, when the Moon again came forth in full and illuminated for him, with a flood of silver light, that strange figure standing within the bushes and hidden by the leaves of the thicket. It fell upon his disheveled hair and seemed to drip down from the cloth wrapped about his shoulders, emphasizing the dark lines of shadow in the folds of his torn garments, bringing out in bold relief his figure on the rocky cliff.

The man was gazing into the depths of the river which spread out at his feet like an enormous fountain of silver, and, when the light returned, he again raised the flute to his lips. The reeds seemed to cut a great wound across the silence of the night, as the notes of pain went forth, falling upon all things, while below the river flowed on, hurling itself against the rocks, bathed in the calm light of the Moon. The unknown thus gave words to his lament:

> Quena that sings my grief,
> Flute that weeps my relief;

This morning,
Fresh and fair,
She went away to the mountain
And was lost
Beyond the endless curve of the horizon.

I sought her in the canebrake,
But she was not there!
Perhaps it was the puma
Who spotted her white garments with blood
Red as the sun at even,
While she was dreaming, unmindful,
Beneath the boughs of a shaded glen.
Since then with my love
I go seeking her.
Flute that sings my grief,
Quena that weeps my relief,
Continue your playing.

Chasca had approached gently toward Llacctan, who, when he had finished, turned toward the old warrior, who thus addressed him as one whispering a prayer in a holy place:

"Skilled singer, only one who has made weep the Inca, who without staff or obligation has been seated in the palace of the Children of the Sun, favorite of princes, sweet dream of Virgins of the Kingdom, when did you return from your journeying?

"The shepherds said that the Father-Sun had taken you up from the Empire that you might play within the walls of his divine mansions. The women of the North said that the Moon herself had banished you, that you cause not the children of men to die of sorrow. The fisherman said they had seen you wandering at night beneath the pale Moon; and the laborers, that the birds, jealous of your singing, had taken away your eyes; the guardians of the Amarucancha, place of serpents, said that, on hearing your music, the serpents had followed and devoured you. Why are you sad and why do you sing by the river?"

"Great is my sorrow, aged noble. No one can understand my grief. Music is weeping. Imagine, if you were a shepherd, having lost, as did Talmay, your flock in the snows; if a laborer in the fields, imagine that the fresh and verdant cornfields, which you had left at the hour when the Sun sinks to rest, you found, at the beginning of a new day, frozen and dead; these were griefs of small consequence."

"Llacctan, your father was sad, you are melancholy; he loved with enthusiasm, you love with desperation; generous was he, prodigal have you been. What a great soul you have to traverse the wide world refusing honors and riches! What carry you in the breast which burns with such enduring flame? What inner fire is it that shows forth in your eyes?"

"I loved my art, but it was not that; I loved pleasure, but it was not that. I love in silence and sorrow, silence and sorrow are they."

"The Father-Sun, in his all-embracing compassion, will bring peace to your spirit, Divine Wanderer."

"The Sun! Know you by chance, ingenuous shepherd, or aged noble, or potter, whoever you may be, know you whether we are the only children of the Sun? Know you whether when he hides himself at night, he goes not to visit other kingdoms? The elder Ticti, he who imprisoned him in his castle, announcing his color, his sorrow and his struggles with other gods, told it to my father: the Sun has other children, other children and other kingdoms. Other children will come; only *she* will never return!"

"Why blaspheme you? Nothing has been so pronounced by the Oracle. Chasca assures you that such is not the case. Be at peace!"

"Chasca? Noble general, you know it also, because you were general of the great king, you were at his side in combats, Chasca, noble general of Huaina Cápac, you too know it!"

And he again sang:

> This morning,
> Fresh and fair,
> She went to the mountain
> And was lost beyond the endless curve
> of the horizon.

Chasca had continued his journey and the melody of the singer was dying away in the distance. The noble warrior hastened his steps to arrive at the bridge of rattan. The Moon rose higher and higher in the heavens, whiter than ever, white as a chalice of snow, which, defying the pull of earth, might issue from the mountain peaks, blue in the night as the darkest depths of the sea. The voice of the quena was growing fainter and fainter, and now, among the forests surrounding the castle, he heard the last strains of that soul in grief weeping itself out beneath the light of that full Moon:

> Perhaps it was the puma
> Who spotted her white garments with blood
> Red as the sun at even,
> While she was dreaming, unmindful,
> Beneath the boughs of a shaded glen.

The warrior having almost vanquished the night and the distance, with infinite sadness and foreboding, hurried on and soon buried himself in the wood in whose depths arose the castle surrounded by a thicket of bushes and vines which crept up the low hill even to the walls of granite.

the journey to the sun

WHEN Sumacc with that placid repose of spirit which marks the cessation of rude toil, and singing a plaintive little melody, when Sumacc returned to the city from the farmland which had been apportioned to him for his marriage with Inquill, the sun was sinking in the west. From time to time laborers crossed his path; like him they were returning from the tasks of the fields and, when a short distance beyond him, inclined their heads, saying respectfully:

"The peace of the Creator be with you."

Soon he arrived at the city and the entrance to the Street of Gold, narrow and straight, sloping downward toward the Plaza of the Sun. From the entrance one could look out over the city and thence Sumacc perceived a spectacle unwonted in the Empire. A crowd, in which garments

of every tribe could be distinguished, filled the Intipampa, inclosure sacred to the Sun-Father. Surely, something of serious import must have occurred. He hastened
his steps and, as he reached the Plaza, an outcry burst
from all lips, and all eyes were fixed on the Street of the
North, whence appeared the figure of a messenger, who
advanced with rapid pace.

"Another messenger! Another messenger!"

The messenger arrived at the Plaza where the crowd
opened a way before him and the officers of the law took
him into the house of the Curaca. Then Sumacc learned
that one messenger had come in the afternoon; and the
wise men of the council had been gathered together
hastily; and, although the priests had said nothing, it was
known by the people that strange and powerful enemies
had invaded the Empire, curious men, unlike any ever
seen before, children of the sea and the Evil One. The
prophecy of Huaina Cápac was about to be fulfilled, that
the bastard Atahualpa would be taken a prisoner and the
Empire subverted by the white and bearded strangers.
The invaders had already assassinated the Inca Huáscar,
sacked Cuzco and carried off the treasures of the temple
and palaces; and furthermore, knowing that in this city
there were treasures also, they were going to invade and
devastate it likewise.

Sumacc entered the house of the Curaca between the
files of officers. The noble youth felt a presentiment of
danger, immediate and inexorable. In the plaza the uneasiness increased; with shouts the people commented
upon the unheard-of event. It was believed by some that
the invasion of foreigners was led by the bastard Atahualpa himself, who had called to his aid the children of
the Evil One to overcome his brother Huáscar. They
recounted bits of his infernal plans. They recalled that
the devil had converted him into a serpent so that he

might escape from his prison in Tumeypampa where he had been overthrown by the armies of his brother.

Some began to call for the Curaca with loud cries and the shouting of the crowd was increasing, when suddenly there arose another cry which congealed the blood and paralyzed all action:

"Another messenger! Another messenger!"

The messenger, with his arms extended, came forward from the hill at the end of the Street of Chincha-Suyu, and soon his lamentations fell like lightning strokes on the people there gathered:

"Misfortune! Misfortune! Misfortune!"

Then was the confusion frightful! People stumbled over one another; some ran to their houses; while others called with loud cries. The mass of people swayed like an immense wave, and a dull roar, with mingled shouts, lamentations, and weeping swept over the Plaza. Women with children bound to their backs made complaint; fathers called their children, separated in the confusion; and no one knew how to escape from the turmoil. The terrified people, palid and transfixed by fear, could pronounce but one phrase:

"The Children of the Evil One . . . The foreigners."

Then there came forth from the house of the Curaca the wise men who spoke to the people from the steps of the building. A tragic silence fell over all, and then Tucuiri-cuc, the messenger of the Inca, who occasionally visited that province, thus addressed the people:

"Children of the Sun, the Empire is in danger, the prophecy has been fulfilled. The sacred city has been destroyed by strangers. The Inca, the Father of Men, the Child of the Sun, has been killed by the children of Supay, the Evil One."

He could continue no longer. A dull roar rose to the heavens. Cries of pain went out from every mouth. The women threw themselves to the ground and wept despairingly, tearing their hair and cursing the strangers. Then for a long time no sound was heard save the long-drawn sob of that multitude wounded by the strange and incomprehensible forces of an adverse destiny. Tucuiricuc continued:

"No longer have we an Inca. We must seek the protection of the Father-Sun. The enemies are marching; soon they will be upon us. Prepare your belongings and await the orders of the Curaca and the Council."

Then the Camayocs, patriarchs of family groups, passed among the people and, with much effort, arranged that each group should return to its dwellings. They gave orders for dispersal and, when the Father-Sun had passed from mortal view, the sacred square was empty.

That night the street lamps were not lighted; darkness invaded the entire city, and the streets were deserted except for an occasional messenger hurrying on his mission, knots of soldiers, or a nobleman pursuing his solitary course. Only on the peak of the sacred mount, looking down over the city, blazed the sacrificial fires attended by the priests. Some youths and many virgins, women of the nobility, had buried themselves alive, in order to accompany the Inca on his journey and to serve him on the way. Among them were the daughter of the Curaca, and twenty sacred Virgins of the Sun.

In the house of the Curaca the Council lasted far into the night, and at midnight the principal men went out to talk to the Camayocs, patriarchal heads of family groups. They had agreed to seek help from the Father-Sun. It would be necessary to abandon the town and go to him. They must take with them all their treasures and cattle, their garments and utensils. The leaders stopped at the door of the house of each patriarch, gave orders, and then continued their way. The patriarchs were each one to give the orders to his forty subordinates and hold them ready for the great journey.

When the shadows began to lighten, and the dew to glisten on the grass, all the families began to go forth in silence. Soon the family groups were seen entering the plazas, and there, with their chiefs at the head, awaited the orders of the Curaca. Among the multitude, the vicuñas raised their graceful, restless heads; the dogs, silent, searched for plunder at the feet of the herds; the alpacas, of silky pelt, in groups stretched themselves out to rest; and the llamas swaying beneath the weight of their cargoes, marched with short steps among the travellers. Silence, scarcely broken by suppressed sobs or the weeping of children, brooded over the people.

The light began to strengthen. The patriarchal leaders gave order that the people go forth after chanting the hymn of the Sun. All hearts were saddened to leave forever the natal hearthstone. Where were they going was the question in each one's heart. The elders thus answered:

"We follow the Sun-Father; He will not abandon us, but will receive us into his mansions. But who knows the way which leads to the Father-Sun? And who knows the place of His abode. Who will show us the way?"

A maiden answered:

"I have dreamed, I have dreamed, that the way leads through beds of bright flowers, beside streams of transparent water, on whose wavelets are reflected the days, the hours, and the moons with their companion months; that all the way is brightened by the warm rays of His effulgence; the path is long but refreshing and at both sides are the palaces of the Emperors. The sweet-voiced melody of the flute accompanies those who journey onward; and one feels neither the weight of the body nor the fatigue of the march."

Then up spoke a potter:

"The Father Sun is behind the mountains. I have heard from one of the messengers of the Inca that behind the high and bleak plateaus of the cordilleras, exists a great river without banks, wherein the Father-Sun sinks nightly to rest. Yes. That is the truth, the Curaca has said that he saw with his own eyes, the Father-Sun pass to his repose in the great lake, when he went to Pachacámac to consult the oracle and purify himself in holy exaltation. The Curaca recounted to my father how in order to reach Pachacámac it was necessary first to pass through the Sacred City and then journey onward sixty days, before arriving at the valley of the holy Oracle. Before the walls the traveller must pause and only after three days of purifying fast could he tread the soil of the Temple of the Lake God. And he told him that the Oracle is on the shore and faces the great lake, in which sinks to rest nightly the Father-Sun. He says the lake is green and roars in unceasing tumult and devours men. Its shores extend on and on surrounding the whole of Tehuantin-suyo, our beloved Empire. To that sacred spot proceed from far-distant peoples persons of highest rank to learn the secrets of their fate. Woe be to those who bring no votive offering, for they shall never know the destiny which time holds for them."

As the potter ceased speaking and the dawn came up, the patriarchal Camayocs appeared. A pale and far-extended light, increasing in intensity at each moment announced the arrival of the Father-Sun. Soon the mount stood out in bold relief, and the tremendous miracle of light burst forth in the east. The people raised their arms in adoration and dolefully chanted the Illarimuy, hymn of all the people, greeting the appearance of the Father-Sun. In a few moments the line of march was organized, toward that distant and unknown country.

Thus began that tragic procession without precedent in the Empire. Only the transportation of forced colonists could be compared to this sublime exodus. What was that procession of thousands of vanquished, leaving their native soil, when their generals had lost in battle and they must obey the commands of the conquering Inca removing permanently to other lands; what was that abandoning of beloved hearthfires, fertile fields, scenes where childhood and youth had slipped tranquilly by, and where the bones of the fathers reposed, compared with this supreme exodus?

The enforced colonists left one region to go to another, but they were taken by soldiers of the Inca, and enjoyed anew the possession of fields and property. What was that lamenting of the brave captains, plaintive wailing of children, and tragic silence of the aged, at leaving the loved places, the mild skies, the well-known trees, to be transferred to an unknown country, when the favor of the Inca was so highly bestowed upon them that they would not willingly return to their distant native soil? What were those fleeting pains at passing from one region to another under the beneficent gaze of the Inca, compared with this overwhelming sorrow at leaving forever the beloved soil, the Inca dead, the Empire destroyed, and without having on earth one whose ear was always bent to the invocations of his children?

Now the people were following with their cattle and possessions an unknown route, guided solely by the faith of the aged, and love for the Curaca. Thus the procession began, the Curaca at the head in his chair of black palm carried on the shoulders of twelve strong soldiers. Behind followed the priests and warriors, Virgins of the Sun, and their attendant Guardians. Then in orderly file came the family groups, each preceded by its patriarchal Camayoc. Many women wore over their shoulders blankets of brilliant colors, others carried their children on their backs. The enormous flocks of llamas, crowded together, carried clothes and implements, treasures, images, jars, weapons and belongings.

Far behind the retinue Sumacc and Inquill journeyed in silence. For none could destiny have apportioned a fate less kind. In one brief instant they had seen vanish as a mist their roseate dreams of happiness. But a few days were lacking, when during the festival of the corn, the Curaca in the name of the Inca would have united the loving pair who would then have been settled on the land which the youth had already cultivated. Relatives had prepared gifts for the festival, and the newlywed pair would have gone to dwell in the house, built by the friendly hands of the community and furnished with gifts from the parents. They had bought fine-woven fabrics of travellers from the North, beautiful pottery from Chimu and from Nazca, necklaces from Rimactampu, garments from the forests far to the eastward, made with feathers of many-colored birds.

The apportioned farm was near a stream whose water descended to the fields with no need of further labor. Already the earth waited with open furrows the seed to multiply in it, and the facundating stream. They would have planted trees to give shade to the beloved one, as she wove for the helpless and prepared food for the blind in the kindly spirit of brotherhood; and the trees would have grown together with sons and daughters, both to be a protection to a happy old age when the fires of youth smolder low and life is a vista of tender memories.

Under the soft skies of late afternoons, in the midst of their murmuring cornfields, while the hills of potatoes pushed the furrows upward in goodly and bounteous crop, cracking the soil in ever-widening seams over the swelling fruit, they together would lift their adoring hearts to the Father-Sun, and would bless his son, the Inca, who such happiness bestowed upon them.

But now Destiny had closed to them the gates opening into the pathway of their dreams and the future was tragic, inexorable, and hopeless. They marched behind the train, pensive and speechless. At times she sobbed disconsolately, and he, having no phrases wherewith to comfort her, let her weep, her head bowed low on her firm breast. Thus the days slipped by.

At times the friends of Sumacc drew near and attempted to console them. They brought the girl a tempting fruit, a flower, or a bird caught by the way. The road was ever hard and seemed endless, when she grew faint, he took her in his arms and carried her long stretches. In the extremity of his solicitude, he bathed her feet in the cool waters of a stream and dried them tenderly. When the cold was unbearable, and the travellers rested, he built great fires to warm her. He gave her the soothing coca to chew, and when they arrived at a brook, he gave her fresh water to drink from the hollow of his hands; in the days of heaviest depression, when water ran low because the travellers had imprudently departed too far from the streams, he sought from his companions a little chicha in order to offer it to her. And thus they journeyed on.

At times, when fatigue overpowered them, they stopped and drank a little water from the nearest stream because all the chicha remaining was saved for the sacrifices. They partook of food but sparingly; a bit of coca, sometimes corn cake, or fruit picked by the way. The first days passed tranquilly. From the villages the people left their houses and followed them. The migrating people followed the footsteps of the Sun westward; each morning the procession journeyed toward the place where the Sun had disappeared the night before beyond the distant mountain. Thus passed twenty days.

Many of the aged women became exhausted and had not the desire to continue: then they agreed to go to their Inca in the world beyond. At nightfall on the peak of the ridge the march was halted; the youths dug the mournful grave; to the wayworn women was given the magic potion which gradually dulled the senses. Surrounded by their treasures, their jars of chicha and of corn, and their festal attire, they seated themselves in humble and compliant attitude within the grave and, while the youths were covering their bodies with earth, repeated the ritualistic phrases of the ceremony. Thus the people, in their sublime exodus toward the Sun, were leaving their trackless path sown with the bones of parents and grandparents. The youths hoped through faith in the elders, and the latter in the love of the Sun-Father.

Every afternoon as dusk was falling the people gathered together and chanted the Illarimuy, sacred hymn to the Sun-Father, in tones of simple and solemn beauty. The women wept softly, while the youths, of square and vigorous countenance, with high cheekbones, invoked the deity in silence. As the last rays of solar light faded, the hymn was ended. Each night the people hoped that, on the day following, the Father-Sun would open to them the gates of the enchanted city. But the day following, as the Father did not reveal himself, they journeyed on.

When at last they felt the end must be approaching, they marched hastily, feverishly, as if they were impelled by some evil spirit dwelling within them. Many did not wish to stop even for food, and they scarcely took time to chew even a few leaves of coca. Some, impatient, hurried to the Curaca and, trying not to show their fears, asked him:

"Taytay, shall we arrive soon at the mansions of our Father, the Sun? Will he open to us the gates of the city? Will he defend us against the white men?"

And the Curaca answered:

"The Sun, our Father, never abandons his people. Some sin has been committed in the kingdom that he has sent those white and ill-omened beings for our chastisement."

"Oh Atahualpa! Atahualpa! Bastard and foreigner!"

At other times, to distract them and revive their courage, after the evening prayer, he had them gather in great circles under improvised tents, where they were to pass the night, surrounded by the flocks, and he or an elder councilor would describe to them the dominions of the Sun. They listened enchanted, and the children, their imaginations fired by the stories, would drop off to sleep, and, little by little, the youths and maidens, all to awaken the following morning filled with renewed hopes.

The land of the Sun, where they were going to be received and dwell forevermore, was an immense country where all men lived in perpetual bliss; they communed daily with the Incas, they had marvellous garments, strange and delicious drinks, and exquisite food. There were fruits, large and sweet, and women more beautiful than those gathered at Cuzco; divine music pervaded the air, birds of multicolored beauty sang tender and haunting melodies, and all the houses were of gold and stones fantastically carved. The beds were of down and the serving-men and women amiable and diligent. Nothing was wanting to satisfy the most exacting desire, and all was illuminated by a radiant light, white as the newly burst cotton boll, and transparent as the ice which congeals in the lakes. The light pervaded everything—body and spirit, objects, flowers, life, dreams, love and desire. It was the kingdom of light, gold, peace; and unalloyed felicity.

Finally they arrived at a range of hills where the penetrating cold of the upland regions gave place to heat. The change seemed to them of good import since there where the climate was warmer must begin the dominions of the Sun. That day Inquill felt happy and smiled. Thus with renewed courage and fervor, they covered long stretches during the day's journey in spite of the heat, and little by little, were descending to the plains. The people, in the few villages passed on the way, wore unfamiliar garments. Every evening at nightfall the travellers chanted the same supplication:

"O Sun! Father of our father, forsake not thy people in their distress, and protect us against the rage of Supay, the Evil One!"

One morning at dawn, they seemed to feel a soft breeze, and to hear a strange, gentle murmur. It was not the roar of pumas, not the multitudes of men; it was somewhat confused and indistinct, but caressing and languid. The murmur came from the side of the Sun, borne on the breeze. Some youths climbed a tiny hill and, when they reached the summit, a cry burst from their lips:

"Cocha! Cocha! Cocha!
A lake! A lake! A lake!"

All the people ascended the hill to behold, with a dull murmur of admiration and enthusiasm, something which they had never imagined; a vast lake without banks, softly blue, was faintly visible in the distance; it was without any doubt that of the abode of the Sun, the famous lake which the Curaca had spoken of and toward which each afternoon the Sun journeyed, as the hour of repose approached.

That morning were six llamas sacrificed and chicha was poured in libation to the honor of the deity. The line of travellers continued its interminable march toward the fertile valley which lay extended at their feet, uninhabited and wild. Upon reaching the shade of its trees, green and copious, they decided to rest a few days before covering the last stage of the journey to the desired shores.

Suddenly the enthusiasm of the people departed. How should they cross that immense river and reach the dwelling place of the Sun? The evening before they surely had seen him hide himself in the waters. It was certain, then, that arriving at the place where they had seen him sink to rest, they would enter into his kingdom. But how to cross that lake, roaring, vast, and imponderable? They agreed to wait, convinced that the Sun would not abandon them. From one moment to the next, they expected to see appear on the horizon some raft directed by the Children of the Sun, who should come for them and take them to the desired country. Thus they waited some days, making sacrifices to the deity every afternoon.

But finally the guardian of the provisions advised the Curaca that he had supply for but three days more and that it was necessary to implore the Father-Sun that he send for his people without further delay. Stopping near to the shore, the Indians felt themselves sinking deeper and deeper into inexpressible dejection. No one doubted that the Father-Sun would save them, but patience was fast changing into melancholy, as they saw that the messengers of the Sun did not arrive. They passed the day exploring the shore seeking some gate in the sea, listening to the voice of the waves, if perchance they might hold for them some whispered word of hope, but nothing gave answer to their unasked question or restraint to their uneasiness ever more intense. As dusk came on, all went down to the water's edge even to the point where the waves wet their feet in order to see if in the gilded wake of the gathering twilight there might not be some sign of the Father-Sun's compassion, but he, enwrapped in clouds, passed from sight behind the watery curtain leaving his suppliant people abandoned to darkness.

Three days passed.

By consuming food sparingly and sending the warriors in search of game, they were able to endure two days more. The third day it was necessary to eat the dried bodies of the ceremonial ducks which had been destined for incense to perfume the sacrifices and garments of the Curaca, elders, and priests.

Sumacc that day was able to catch a fish which he brought to Inquill, fresh and alive, with glistening silvery back and great round eyes. Inquill, in the midst of her sadness and fatigue, clapped her hands with joy for one brief moment; she had never seen so pretty a creature.

Hunger threatened. That last afternoon, when the limit of endurance had been reached, the invocation to the Sun was made weeping. From that believing people, covering the beach in broadly extended line, gilded by the last rays of the dying Sun, went forth one great cry of grief, heartrending and sincere:

"Father! Father! Father! Forsake not thy people! Tell us the way to thy marvellous kingdoms!"

But none answered that cry of grief and despair, and as the Sun slowly sank from sight, the weeping increased and finally rose above the roar of the sea. There was one moment, that during which the Sun kissed the horizon, in which hope flared up like that last spark among dying embers, and they waited to see the Sun come forth and speak to them with the same kindly magnanimity that he had shown toward Manco Cápac. They ceased their lamentations, but with rude indifference the enormous disc sank from sight into the sea. Then they threw themselves to the ground, disconsolate. Some called to others. The children, embracing their parents, wept with terror and for a long time on that desolate beach were heard only broken sobs and lamentations.

As night fell there met in council the Curaca and the four elder councilors, the heads of families, priests, and old men. The full Moon was brilliant and seemed to float in a sapphire sea. They all mounted the low hill which overlooked the valley and there held lengthy council. Some thought that they should continue to wait on the shore and hold their faith in the Sun. Food could be procured in that same valley by hunting during the first few days, then later sowing and reaping, besides catching the fish which gleamed amid the waves with silvery sheen. Others thought they should plunge into the sea so that when the Father-Sun should see them in danger He would save them.

Then they brought back in memory their distant hearthstones, their fertile fields with crops half-grown, the peace of that far-away dwelling place. How much better it would have been to remain and receive there death at the hands of the foreigners, men with beards of snow!

After a moment of silence a voice spoke forth in the calm peace of the moonlit night. It was that of an aged man with eyes clouded through the course of the years, a famous councilor, whose task it was at Cuzco to determine the feasts of Cápac Raymi at the time when the image of the Sun was enclosed in the sacred square to receive the homage of the people. Thus he spoke:

"The Father-Sun has forsaken us! He is all-powerful and could save us. Who knows if it may not be that the other god stronger than he has overcome him in battle? From this Sun we can hope for nothing more. Already he has permitted the strangers to enter Cuzco and destroy his image as well as the images of the Emperors, to carry away the doors and jars of gold, to carry away the fringe, symbol of the regal power, and the sacred plumes of Coraquenque. He has permitted the bastard to assassinate the son of Huaina Cápac and in his turn has permitted the Evil One to kill Atahualpa. He does not concern himself with us and it is better to die and seek the

Emperors. They will hear our supplication and will never forsake us. There shall we find the four brothers Ayar, the founders of the Empire, and the Emperors, their children!"

The words of the aged councilor seemed wise to the people and they answered:

"Let us go in search of the Emperors! Let us go!"

Then all the group moved with sombre determination: the men of strong arm descended from the height and with their implements dug huge trenches in the moist sand. They worked with feverish haste, while the elders had gone to carry the decision to the camp of the travellers. At dawn the work was almost completed, only a few portions of earth remaining to be removed. And at noon beneath the rays of the Sun, fierce in their intensity, the work was finished.

Some desired to dig the tomb of their mothers, others for the young women whom they had hoped to marry, and others for decrepit fathers who had somehow endured the rigors of the journey. That day no word was spoken: all were thinking of the last journey, without fear, but with profound dejection, in an abandonment of solitary meditation the hour of sunset arrived and the people prepared to die. With great effort they secured a quantity of the benumbing drink sufficient to lull into drowsy insensibility the women and children. The Curaca and a group of councilors assisted by six vigorous youths took upon themselves the duty of covering one by one, two by two, or however they wished to undertake that last journey, those whose love death itself could not mar.

And as the sky began to soften into tinge of ruddy glow they chanted the hymn to the Sun and the last supplication. The Indians, having arranged their treasures and their garments, and adorned themselves with their most cherished finery, went down into the terraced trenches.

There, after taking draughts of the liquor in order not to feel the suffocation of the journey, they seated themselves and, little by little, passed into the heavy and unfeeling sleep which betokens the merciful languor preceding oblivion.

The earth was slowly heaped over them where they sat in attitudes of supplication and soon the ground was again level. The task required the entire afternoon. Some, before descending to the trenches, embraced one another and took leave weeping, their grief allayed only when the earth covered their inert bodies. Finally there remained only those who had buried the others.

Inquill had not wished to be interred and waited for her loved one to perform the rite. When Sumacc had thrown the last shovelful of earth on the last Indian, he turned his eyes toward Inquill. Only those two were left. Seating themselves on the mound by the only trench which remained open, they looked out over the sea, green and boundless. Sumacc, without looking at Inquill, clasped her hands in his and wept over them, saying:

"Heavy and full of sorrow is this labor; privileged obligation to be the last to pass into the dominions of the Sun. One by one I have interred all the men and all the women. Now there remain only the two of us."

"And now, I too must go," answered Inquill softly without betraying a tinge of emotion in her countenance. "Bury me."

The Indian made no answer. What could he say? He could not delay; to prolong the grief of his beloved would but intensify the sacrifice! She must go, as her people who had preceded her, to join herself to the Father-Sun, in the radiant palaces of gold.

"Remain with me, Inquill, I beg you, yet a while to be my companion," cried out the Indian youth, his voice trembling and desolate. "But a little time and you will join the Sun, and although we shall be reunited there, would you not rather wait here in the land where we have loved? Does it not grieve your heart to leave this world where the moments of our love have passed so hastily? The palaces of the Sun are doubtless marvellous and more magnificent than those of earth, but, for some reason I do not understand, I feel a deep sorrow at leaving it."

And his moist eyes looked out in contemplation, over the deep and far-reaching valley, whose verdure gave a note of joy to that field of death and sorrow. Below he could see the shining streams winding like silver serpents through the green thickets; but no song of a bird could be heard. There were only the two souls and two bodies in all that region, which gave evidence of life on earth. With their arms entwined in one embrace, they walked a few steps over the mound, above that supulchered humanity, the earth still warm from an afternoon Sun, mild and misty. But when the Sun began to decline over the sea, Inquill looked at the open trench at her feet.

"Let us go," repeated Sumacc, as an echo.

Then he took from the leather wallet of his belt a tiny jar of clay on whose surface images of the household gods had been baked, and gave to Inquill to drink of the liquor of peace, that liquid which lulls the senses and sweetens death, and which he had preserved as a precious jewel. The loved one took the bitter draught and descended into the terraced trench with solemn dignity. Sumacc placed at her side whatever was necessary for the journey, sandals of finest texture, jars of chicha preserved especially by him, clothes to protect her body, and in her hand the tribute for the Sun.

"Now I am going, Sumacc; now I am going." Her voice grew faint. "Kiss me!"

Standing, the two united their lips in one long kiss,

lingering, silent, and solemn, until Inquill's head fell from his lips as a ripe fruit, and her body lost its strength.

When Sumacc had thrown the last shovelful of earth upon the body of Inquill he felt a strange sensation. Now he could not talk for there was no one to listen. Then he had an impulse to bury himself, but how could he do so? He threw himself on the tomb of Inquill, his adored one, and wept a long time. The Sun began to set.

Then he felt another sensation which he had never before experienced. For the first time he was afraid. It seemed to him that from the closed tomb came forth words and groans which mingled with the murmur of the waves. He was the only survivor of that people abandoned by divine mercy. He wished to open the grave of his beloved to unite himself with her, but the fear of disturbing her slumber prevented him. Then he looked at the Sun: he saw how, red and indifferent, it was approaching the waters, and how the shadows in the mountain ranges were deepening.

A pain, a sudden and powerful unrest took possession of him. Objects seemed transparent to him, and he could not feel the weight of his body. He remembered that for two days he had eaten nothing but coca. A drowsiness was creeping over him; he stood upright. Flocks of white birds crossed the sky above him seeking regions he could not know, and his thoughts became confused with shadows. A persistent memory, the memory of his beloved Inquill haunted him; he fancied he heard her voice, calling him from the earth.

The Sun was gone.

Then his idea of abandonment became clear. Fear of living above the tomb of all his people filled him with dread, and he began to weep as a child and call on the Sun. Unintentionally he had thrown himself again upon the tomb of Inquill which he tore with his hands as he called to his loved one, but now she did not respond. Again his thoughts were confused; then he seemed to see a light in the depth of the sea, which appeared and then disappeared. Enormous fantastic shadows filed before him in the roaring waves. Again he stood erect and approached to the edge of the water.

Now he took no notice of things, but began to weep brokenly and to pour forth lamentations, calling upon the Sun, until he lost the very substance of his thoughts. He advanced into the waves with uncertain steps: the first threw him down; he struggled a little, then others broke over him; he uttered broken words which the roar of the waves obliterated and the body of the last member of this courageous Quechua band sank forever.

The Moon in its sapphire setting again looked down on the place where now a people lay buried. And a white bird in the tranquil air crossed the shining wake, flying toward the dim horizon.